Retrieved from the Future

Retrieved from the Future

John Seymour

The characters and some of the towns in this book are imaginary and are not intended to represent any real person or actual place.

Published in the United Kingdom in 1996 by
New European Publications Limited
14–16 Carroun Road
London SW8 1JT, England

Cover design Lloyd Allen
Project Management and editing Margaret Allen
Typesetting Margaret Allen
Proof-reading John Rattray

British Library Cataloguing in Publication Data

A full catalogue record for this book is available from the British Library

ISBN 1–872410–05–7 paperback

Printed in Great Britain by Biddles Limited, Guildford, Surrey

Also by John Seymour

Boys in the Bundu
The Hard Way to India
Round About India
One Man's Africa
Sailing into England
The Fat of the Land
Self Sufficiency
The Complete Book of Self Sufficiency
The Woodlander
The Smallholder
The Shepherd
The Countryside Explained
The Love of the Land
The Forgotten Arts
The Forgotten Household Arts
The Self Sufficient Gardener
Voyage into England
Far from Paradise
Blueprint for a Green Planet
England Revisited
Bless'ed Isle
On My Own Terms
Seamarks (Poetry)

The Companion Guide to East Anglia
The Companion Guide to the Coast of S. E. England
The Companion Guide to the Coast of N. E. England
The Companion Guide to the Coast of S. W. England

Preface

Every city-based civilisation before our own has collapsed. Why should we suppose that ours should be exempt?

John Seymour claims that he has retrieved from the Future the story of what happens to one little corner of England when this inevitable crash occurs.

Our twentieth century civilisation is unprecedently fragile. Billions of people live in huge conurbations depending for every minute of their lives on a tiny handful of farmers and fishermen to feed them, and a vast fleet of diesel lorries to bring the food to them, often over great distances and from far countries. The whole complex that keeps the city people alive depends upon oil. Oil to grow, catch and carry the food; oil to generate the electricity to keep them lighted and warm; oil to work the pumps that keeps water running out of taps.

This book is the story of what will, inevitably, happen if there is any interruption in the supply of oil. It could happen today – it could happen tomorrow. It is more likely to happen in twenty or thirty years' time.

Maybe we could learn lessons from this story which – if we heed them – could prevent this rather sad and violent story from happening at all! I hope to God we do. Maybe, by acting sensibly now, we can actually shape the Future, and ensure decent lives for our children and grandchildren.

For the sake of our descendants we should read – and heed – this book.

John Seymour

This book is dedicated to the memory of the millions of innocent people who died prematurely all over the world owing to the stupidity and lack of awareness of their leaders.

Bungay 20 - -

Prologue

by the Publisher

This is the first book published in East Anglia, and probably England and – who knows? – perhaps in Europe and the World since the great CRASH.

When I found it possible to re-open the ancient printing house here in Bungay (which had originally been founded by an ancestor of mine) I decided that we should start publishing books again (although God knows there are enough old ones mouldering away in abandoned libraries up and down the country) and that the first one should be an account of what happened in this small corner of England during and after the CRASH. And also, perhaps, more hopefully of how the foundations of a new – and we hope better – civilisation are being laid.

I searched for an historian to write such a volume but none could be found. Apparently the survival value of historians was not so great as that of, for example, small farmers. But a farmer I did find. Mr Robert Hurlock, who had already begun to write – and encourage people to contribute to – such a book.

My special thanks are due to Miss Elizabeth Keeble. It was she who recorded the accounts of those of our contributors who were too busy, or too unused to writing, to write down their accounts for themselves.

Miss Keeble, as indeed all of us, was anxious to preserve the ancient dialect of the coastal area of East Suffolk, and she has gone to great pains to transcribe as accurately as possible the words of, for example, Mr Dike Randle.

Lastly, I would like to render my heartfelt thanks to all the people who contributed, in their own scarce time, to this historical book.

John Childs, Printer and Publisher
Bungay
Suffolk
The Confederation of East Anglia

12 June 20 - -

Chapter One

by Bob Hurlock

This is going to be an informal sort of a book – we're none of us writers – the most I ever wrote before were reports in the army.

I'm not going to describe the CRASH here, or what led up to it. Everyone who reads this, if anybody does, will have lived through it, and will probably know more about it than I do. I can claim to some extent, though, that "I told you so!". I always knew it would happen. It just staggered me that Western politicians couldn't see, when China soared to economic power in the 1990s, that its demand for oil – and ability to bid for it – would starve the West, and the Western economies would come crashing down. But I have to admit that even I didn't anticipate the Jihad of the Shia Muslims, nor realise that, when the Shia fundamentalists swept down into the Arabian Peninsula, they would quite destroy all the oil wells.

But they did – and our already tottering system came crashing down.

I must just set the scene, though, for our own particular little private drama.

Gretford is a small town about two miles from my farm. It forms a natural centre for a piece of country (although it is not geographically in the centre of it) of about ten miles by ten, which contains seven small villages or hamlets, and which is bounded by the sea on one side, the River Gret on another, and the River Mudde on a third. There are only three roads into this area from the rest of England: two crossing the rivers on bridges and another on the narrow isthmus of land where the rivers nearly meet. Beyond this isthmus, and about five miles to the west of it, is the small town of Randersfield on the old A12 highway which went from London to Great Yarmouth. Much of the Gretford area is light sandy soil, a lot of it planted up by the old Forestry Commission with Scots or Corsican Pine.

In December of *20 - -* we had a Conservative government in England and all the usual things were happening – strikes, bankruptcies, thousands being flung out of work and the inner cities decaying. Plenty of crime and all that and nobody seemed to know what to do about it. It was obvious – to me at least – that the whole thing was due for collapse anyway. And it was the coldest winter I'd seen in my lifetime and that made it all a lot worse.

But I was quite unprepared for the speed at which the whole thing fell to pieces. And then the Prime Minister made this speech on the television. There were only a few days reserve of food in the big cities, she said. The army was busy requisitioning food from the farmers but it might be some time before it reached the people. There was enough oil for the army and essential services, provided nobody else used it. Road transport was virtually halted by the weather and the fact that all road workers were on strike. Troops were trying to clear the snow on the motorways but they were too stretched to clear all of it. The railways were practically at a standstill, mostly because of frozen points, but a series of strikes had disrupted them anyway. The merchant navy was still functioning and bringing oil and coal from the North, but not enough to meet anything like the demand. People should stay at home – stay in bed, to keep warm – in fact just hold on until food and fuel could be got to them. She ended her speech by saying that martial law had been declared throughout the United Kingdom; anyone would be shot immediately who failed to obey a policeman or a soldier, and the British people, who had always proved so good in trouble and emergency, would no doubt pull through now. And that is the last time we were to hear her voice.

Next morning I decided to go to Gretford.

I walked in; and quite a job it was too, for the snow was two feet deep at least and drifting. I took my old labrador with me, Flash. It was funny to see him lollopping over the deep snow. At least he wasn't worrying about any crisis.

Except for the deep snow, Gretford seemed very much as normal. People were busily shovelling snow off the pavements in front of their houses. Gretford had a proper baker's shop and I noticed that it was open and doing a fine trade. Well, the wrapped-sliced-pap van won't get through for a day or two, I thought. Old Alum, the manager of the supermarket, was standing outside its closed door talking to about a dozen people. I went to hear what he was saying and it was that he intended to keep the shop closed until further notice to prevent hoarding.

"But I haven't been hoarding!" shrilled old Mrs Fothergill.

"Maybe, but there's plenty that have," said Alum. "I'm not going to open 'til I get orders from authority."

Outside *The Crown* stood old Dugdale. Major Dugdale he liked to be called. He was an old regular army dugout, and a great busybody in Gretford. He was talking to the vicar, Reverend Smythe, and Clifford Brown. Dugdale waved his hand to me. I went over to them. All three were wearing astrakhan hats and looked like Russian Commissars. By God it was cold.

"What do we do now, Hurlock?" said Dugdale.

"Go on much as we were going on before, I suppose," I said.

"I don't think that'll be possible," said Clifford Brown. Brown was the local manager of London Farming – a large city-based corporation which owned ten thousand acres around here. London Farming had been trying to buy my little farm off me for years and Brown hated me because I wouldn't sell. They even offered me a good job as one of their managers – with a private aeroplane. How about that!

"How much wheat have you got in your silos, Brown?" I asked him.

"A few thousand tonnes – how much have you got in yours?"

"A few thousand tonnes – how much have you got in yours?"

"Enough to keep me and the missus 'til harvest come again," I said. I always tended to talk Suffolk to people like Brown, who had no roots anywhere – not even in London.

"Did you hear the Prime Minister's speech?" said the vicar.

"Yes – she told us all to go to bed and stay there," I said. "Churchill told us to fight on the beaches – Mrs G. tells us all to go to bed."

"We're going to have a meeting, at three o'clock this afternoon, in the church," said Dugdale. "Sir Charles has agreed to be chairperson of it. We've sent word to all the villages around. Meanwhile Sir Charles is in command."

"What of?" I asked.

"Us."

The vicar walked off.

"The vicar was against us having a secular meeting in his church but we persuaded him," said Dugdale. "It's the only building big enough if many people turn up."

"He insists on holding a short service first," said Brown.

"And meanwhile," said Major Dugdale, "headquarters are in the big room in *The Crown*."

"Is the bar open?" I asked, with perhaps too much fervour.

"No. And when it is, beer will be strictly rationed."

Five purposeful men, looking like a deputation, were advancing from the Methodist chapel. They were all prominent non-conformists, led by Gurling, a man who had been an honest small farmer until his farm had been snapped up by London Farming. Now he held some sort of sinecure under the Ministry of Agriculture, and spent his time driving round in a little van doing nothing. It was not his fault that he had been forced to sell his farm; it was only my army pension and a little money that Jessie had inherited that enabled us to keep ours. But Mr Gurling was up-in-arms.

"What's this I hear that a meeting is going to be held in the Anglo-Roman church?" he demanded.

"Well Mr Gurling – the church is the only building big enough to hold everybody."

I was delighted to see that, even in England's final death throes, the age-old conflicts still held their ground. In the end, it was arranged that the vicar should hold his service after the meeting and not before, and an equivalent service should be held in the nonconformist chapel.

I walked back to the farm to feed the stock. It was snowing again. I suggested to Jessie that she should go to the meeting instead of me. I had work to do on the farm. She could ride there on a horse. But she didn't want to leave the children for some reason – although they would have been perfectly all right – and so I drove back in the Land-Rover myself. This time I didn't take Flash because I couldn't take him into the House of God.

When I got back to the village I found some thirty or forty people, looking rather sheepish besides very cold, standing in a group and being addressed by a young man called "Save-Soul" Jones. "Save-Soul" was testifying at the top of his voice. A little group of men and women stood behind him: the women with that strange rather bloodless look that very pious young women seem to have. They were a group of Primitive Baptists who frequently took the advice to go into the highways and byways to preach the Gospel.

From the Parish church I could hear the drone of the organ. Could it be that the vicar was cheating? There was a throng of people outside the church. It amazed me how many people had managed to get there in spite of the snow and the lack of motor transport.

"Save-Soul" ended up with one last vehement exhortation and we all began to file into the church.

Never since the Middle Ages, I imagine, had that church been so full. There were people standing in the aisles. A platform had been improvised near the lectern, and on this sat Sir Charles Lloyd, the local big-wig; old Dugdale; Clifford Brown; and the Reverend Bill Smythe.

Sir Charles got up, coughed, and banged the table.

People shut up.

"You all know what has happened," he said, in his best Conservative Party Rally voice. "England – our beloved country – is in serious trouble. We won't go into why, or whether it was elements within the country that have brought us to these straits or elements outside. We know transport has broken down, in the big cities there is no food, no light or heat – no electricity. We could be on the verge of total breakdown. The news today was even worse than it was last night when the Prime Minister spoke. There have been serious riots in London and other places and the military have had to open fire on several occasions. What will happen now we can only guess. Now probably all will come right in the end. This glorious old country has triumphed before and will triumph again. Maybe in a few weeks everything will return to normal and we will be able to go on living our lives again.

"But we must be alive to every contingency. Supposing it is several weeks before a supply of oil and petrol does get through to us? We must prepare now for the worst. I have up on this platform with me here the Reverend Bill Smythe, who has kindly lent us his church – and who knows whether we should not return to God in our extremity. Maybe we have been a heathen country too long. Then there is Major Dugdale to represent, if I may put it so, the military power; and lastly Mr Clifford Brown, the manager of the local farms of London Farming which is, of course, by far the biggest employer in the district. They both have special problems which I will allow them to put to you themselves. I will now hand you over to Major Dugdale."

But a man sitting near the front got up and shouted:

"Excuse me, but may I ask by what democratic right you have taken the Chair?"

Sir Charles went red in the face. He got to his feet and said: "Well, look here, firstly I'm Chairman of the Community Council . . ."

"That's only Gretford!" shouted someone.

"Well – yes. But somebody has to take the initiative. I was asked to take the Chair and I've taken it."

"Who asked you?"

"Sit down – shut up!" came from the back somewhere at the interrupter. Sir Charles was now getting even redder. "Look here," he said, "let's get on with the meeting. I don't want the job. We can have a proper election for a council in due course if it needs it – if we find things get worse than we thought. Meanwhile, somebody has got to do something. Now, shall I get on with the meeting or shall I not? Let us have a show of hands. For me getting on with it – hands up please."

Up went most of our hands. We weren't going to be balked out of this entertainment.

"Right then – motion carried. Now then, Major Dugdale, will you tell us what you know about the military aspect of it all."

Sir Charles sat down and Dugdale stood up. "Simply," he said "that the country is under martial law. As you know I command the Territorial Army in the area and therefore, until I receive orders from the regular Army, I will assume command. Meanwhile all Territorials will report to me in the drill hall at Randersfield. I shall be there this afternoon and will make that my headquarters until the regular Army come and take over or things return to normal. That's all I've got to say."

A somewhat shocked silence followed this.

Sir Charles stood up and said: "Now Mr Clifford Brown, as the chief employer and agriculturist here, has something to say to you."

Brown stood up. A pale, small, man with several letters after his name, BSc. Agric and all the rest of it, and he was no more a farmer than my cat; this is what farming had come to in England. Owing to successive Governments' policies of cheaper and ever cheaper food, and yet higher and higher wages, only the vast organisations had been able to afford the massive mechanisation needed to produce food cheaply enough to compete.

Brown was unsmiling, humourless – as dead as a door nail inside: a man of figures, nothing more – a calculating machine. The machine opened its mouth and out came a lot of clichés.

"There are one or two little matters that require a certain amount of consideration," he said. "The first matter that is

giving us a bit of a headache is the matter of wages. To put it
bluntly, unless I am very much mistaken, there won't be any
money on pay-day."

"Shame!" said a voice.

"Well we cannot make money. And all banks have been closed.
There is nothing we can do for the time being. As a temporary
expedient I would suggest that we credit workers with the amount
that they earn and transfer the money to them when normalcy
returns."

"When will that be?" said a voice.

"The other small matter that is exercising my attention is the
matter of, er, cows." One expected to hear him say 'Milk-
producing Units'. "Er – cows. London Farming is milking two
hundred and twenty at Batford Hall. As you know, the electricity
supply has been cut off. Fortunately we have an alternative
source of power to drive the milking machines—a diesel engine.
But there is the matter of power. If we are to get the harvest in
we must not squander our fuel. We do not know when we may
get some more. Therefore I must ask you – as many men as can
do it – to come to the Hall and learn to hand-milk."

He then went on to say that there was also the problem of the
distribution of the milk. London Farming milk had previously
gone in bulk to London. The milk that the Gretford people drank
had come from Ipswich. Now the people round about would have
to drink local milk. But how were they to get it? Oil could not be
squandered delivering it to them. They would have to walk or
cycle to Batford Hall every day, that was all. Then there were
other problems. Like many of the cows in England in those days,
the Batford herd never saw the light of day. They were
maintained by what was known as 'zero grazing'. This was the
practice of harvesting grass and other green stuff by foraging
machines and carrying it to the cows indoors. The huge fields
that London Farming had made by bulldozing all our hedges and
ditches were completely unfenced; how were the cows to be
controlled if they went out to graze?

I had hated to see, as I had seen ever since the second war with

Germany, the yeomen of England transplanted by bigger and bigger operators until there was hardly a proper farmer left in the country. I had hated to see the man replaced by the machine. All in the name of efficiency, but nobody ever asked: efficient for what? I could see the life being sucked out of our land – our people, our nation – just to make dividends. Dividends for nameless, faceless people who had nothing in the least to do with the land of England.

Everyone in the place knew of this crankery of mine. So I suppose no-one was surprised when I got up and said: "Mr Chairman, may I make a suggestion. Why not London Farming issue their cows out to anybody in the district who knows about cows. Every parish could then have a small herd properly looked after by a local man – he could see they got milked and distribute the milk around to the people near him. You could thus solve three problems: how to feed the cows, how to milk them, and how to deliver the milk."

There was a silence. Then Sir Charles spoke to Brown and Brown said: "I would thank Mr Hurlock for his suggestion, but I really do not think it would be practicable."

There was a small titter of laughter. And that was that.

Brown went on to say that there was no immediate shortage of food. London Farming still had some wheat in its elevators; this could be ground by hammer-mill and people could make their own bread. He would arrange for the local shopkeepers to allow people flour, and other produce, on credit, until such time as London Farming could get to a bank and pay its workers. Meanwhile, so that everybody could derive the benefit of whatever was going, anybody at all could report to London Farming and be given either a job or, if no job was possible, free credit notes which afterwards could be transformed into cash. Actually there was very little work to do at the moment, but if the oil supply did run out, and there was any considerable delay in replenishing it, then there would be a great demand for hand labour. He hoped that situation would not arise, however. Certainly a supply of oil would come from somewhere.

Sir Charles then got up and said that, if the meeting accepted his suggestion, the district could be administered by Brown, Dugdale, and himself, together with other people whom they might appoint, until after harvest. Then, say about April, if the country at large had not returned to normal, and normal Government had not been resumed, they could have an election for a new council. The body of the meeting agreed to this, or most of it did, and the meeting broke up.

With that I got in my Land-Rover and made off back to my farm.

Chapter Two

by Jessie Hurlock

(From the papers that were found hidden in Sibford Maltings
by Jessie Hurlock before she was taken away to be shot.)

Well, here I sit in these dam' maltings – which incidentally I
caused to be converted into a refugee hostel in the first place, but
I never thought I'd end up as a refugee myself. I'm more than
a refugee – I'm a prisoner. I can see, under our precious "army",
this place slowly converting from a refugee camp into a
concentration camp.

I suppose it's funny, and I try to see the funny side, but it's not
so dam' funny really. The other day a charming gentleman from
the "army" came and told me to write a letter to Bob (that's my
husband) telling him that the kids and I would be shot if he tried
to escape. I gave him the two finger salute.

Anyways, I'm anticipating my story.

I'm writing this so that maybe in future times, when people are
kinder, more peaceable, more rational and more loving, someone
will read it and understand, in some little way, what happened to
us. Oh yes – I have good friends outside who are going to hide
this material and so maybe it will survive.

First of all – who am I and where did I start from?

Well it might seem strange that a lady who was a pacifist,
anarchist, women's lib, anti-nuke, save-the-whales libertarian and
all that package should marry a straight guy like Bob! Well there

was ol' Bob – ex-Winchester, ex-regular British Army and, when I met him, a prosperous farmer – and there was I, born in California, hippy as hell, cookie as a fox, smoking grass like a municipal incinerator. I was just visiting these groovy guys at Bungay Horse Fayre, and who should roll in but this fascinating English gent with a red hankie round his neck driving a horse and cart – no, for God's sake – two horses and a cart; one horse in front of the other. Get that.

Anyway it all happened, he got me on the gin, I got him on the grass – in two senses I suppose – we made it behind a haystack and he changed me and I changed him. Don't know who changed the most – probably never will know. And I got him by the scruff of the neck and dragged him to the altar. Quick – before he could get away.

Well I'm not going to tell the dreary ol' story of the CRASH and how it happened. Suppose if anybody ever does read what I'm writing they'll have been through it – or their parents will have and will have bored them rigid with the story of it all. I don't think it was just "the oil". Believe me, I'm a farmer's wife and I think it was the grub, the nosh, the tucker or whatever you limeys call it. The food ran out, and everybody was so used to food just apparently growing on supermarket shelves that they didn't notice it was short until it was far too late.

I think it would have blown up anyways. There was the hellish boredom of it all. People stuck all their lives to office desks or factory benches doing the same monotonous job which they never see the beginning or end of. Of course there were strikes, and more strikes. Can you blame 'em? The only thing that kept it all going was the counter-economy – the black market.

Of course ol' Bob was always a prophet of doom.

"What will happen when the oil runs out?" was his parrot-cry. All the huge agribusinesses, and England was full of 'em by the end of the 1990s, were hooked on oil-derived chemicals. It wasn't the tractor fuel that was the problem – it was the fixed nitrogen that was used for fertiliser and the vast array of poisons that had to be sprayed on all the crops. Why, wheat was often sprayed eight or nine times during its period of growth by our neighbours – London Farming. And it was nothing for them to dump half a ton of nitrogen on an acre of land. Phew! Of course they grew a helluva lot of wheat. Three tons to the acre if everything went right. Bob used to say it took them eight calories of energy to get a calorie of energy in the form of bread to the table, and that was about right I guess. We were the wise virgins of course. We contented ourselves with two tons to the acre of good wheat – and we didn't use an ounce of chemicals on it. Why? – we were organic freaks weren't we? And there were plenty more of us up and down the country, hanging on in spite of every kind of discouragement from the dam' silly government. Given the chance, we could have saved England. We weren't given it. Anyone could see big-city civilisation had got to break down. Way back when I was a sophomore at Berkeley I could sense that – we all could if we had any nous. After all, you don't have to have an honours degree in history (which I've got incidentally) to know that civilisation after civilisation has gone bang since the world began – why should ours be spared? Oh yes, the chemicals worked; we had grain and butter mountains and wine and milk lakes and God knows what-all. Only the poor old Russians didn't seem to be able to make out. But for a while they didn't need to – we dumped our surpluses on them. America dumped wheat on them until they got hooked on it. Then – bang! In 20 - - the Yankee grain crop failed: no grain for Russia, no surplus grain to feed cattle, and – what d'ye know – the Europeans had a bad year too and the fertiliser was in the wind-machine! Which is a polite way of saying the shit was in the electric fan. Then the great war between Shias and Sunnis broke out and the Arab oil wells were destroyed.

Things crawled along in Europe until December 20 - - and then came the Bad Winter. My God, that caught old England on the hop. The tankers couldn't load from the off-shore oil platforms because of the weather, the railways came to a halt (they were having a strike anyway but when the men came back to work the points were all frozen up), the road workers struck and there was

nobody but the army to clear the roads. Of course it was a
heaven-sent opportunity for nearly everybody to down-tools. The
power workers were out at the drop of the first snow-flake. The
refinery workers, that is the oil-rig men, came out. It must have
been frozen hell working out on those dam' rigs anyways.

It all happened so quickly, that's what gets me. The whole
dam' thing just fell to pieces like a house built of cards. One
moment England – the whole world in fact – was jogging along.
Then – suddenly – no electric, no oil, no coal, no railway, no
road traffic, no newspapers and – very, very quickly – no food!
The supermarket shelves were empty. I remember Bob quoting to
me a stinging little verse. It so struck me that I scribbled it down
on the wall by the telephone:

> I saw in a vision
> The worm in the wheat
> And in the shops nothing
> For people to eat
> Nothing for sale
> In Stupidity Street.

Well the whole world had been living in Stupidity Street for
just too long.

Of course with Bob and me it was a matter of "dam' you Jack;
we're OK". We had cut ourselves off from the central electricity
supply years before – we had no less than three of those big
Canadian wind machines. We had solar heating, of course, but
we also had tons and tons of wood to fuel our Stanley Stove. And
there was plenty more in the woods and we knew how to get it.
And we had our methane gas plant fed with cow and pig manure,
and it gave us more than we could burn. We had big ricks of
wheat ready to thresh, barley and oats and a big clamp of spuds –
you name it, we had it. Ol' Bob, and me of course, insisted on
dragging a lot of what we had down to Gretford in the wagon
behind two horses – we even built a sled when the snow got bad
– to dish out to the old ladies and people with lots of children.

Listening to the radio was unbelievable. In three days it all
went pow! That silly woman of a prime minister made a silly

speech – told us all to go to bed and stay there until the situation was "regularised"; nobody was to leave the house except on "essential business". Next day we were told the country was under martial law; everybody was to keep calm. How the hell a mum keeps calm when there isn't any grub to give to the kids I can't see. Then the London radio packed up. All we had was some fool of a man named Lieutenant-Colonel John Nightingale giving off from Birmingham about people keeping calm and all that. Then that cut off. I've got to hide this now – some dam' silly soldier has walked in.

Another Day

It would not be true to say that life went on just as usual at Cragpit Farm but, surprisingly, for several weeks it went on very pleasantly. Except that is, for the very serious disagreement I had with Bob.

There was so much work to do that none of us had much time to worry about the rest of the world outside Gretford District, nor, indeed, had we much time to concern ourselves with what went on inside it. All we could think about was the farm.

The impending fuel shortage, of course, forced us to modify our farming plans considerably. Bob and I were about the only people, I believe, who really thought it would last. Everybody else had a sublime faith that "the Americans" or "the Arabs" or God Almighty Himself would come to England's rescue.

My belief is that everybody, except the last one, had plenty of trouble themselves. And who knows what troubles He was having either?

I moved heaven and earth to lay in as big a variety of seeds as I possibly could. I drove the horse and cart into Woodbridge and went to Notcutts, the very good seed merchants there, and bought a vast selection of vegetable and crop seeds. I paid for these, believe it or not, in bacon and ham! Money just did not have any meaning any more so I took a load of salt pig meat in with me.

That trip was the best trip I ever made in my life. It was the most valuable thing, I believe, I could have done.

The children didn't have to go to school any more and they were pleased as hell about that. If a farm home life is varied and interesting enough, as ours always was, no farm child wants to leave it and go to some dreary school. I believe that the best thing that the Disaster brought to us was that it killed, for ever I hope, that dreadful academic "education" that stultified generations of children, kept them indoors when they should have been outdoors, bored them to death and rendered them quite unfit for any life at all except for becoming clerks or factory hands. Or, if they were very "bright" which is another way of saying had no imagination but encyclopaedic memories, turned them into perfectly useless "professionals" or, even worse, academics.

One person we'd all underestimated was old Dugdale. He mobilised his territorials at Randersfield, which had been the territorial depot, and issued them all out with weapons and ammunition. He then, off his own bat, put pickets on the three bridges leading over the Mudde and the Gret and had men patrolling the banks of the two rivers to stop people swimming across.

There was a lot of controversy about this. I, for one, was completely against it. "What bloody right have we got," I said "to stop English people moving about their own country?"

"Look, there's twenty million people in London and Birmingham," said Bob. "Do you want 'em all swarming over those bridges into this county and eating everything we've got like a plague of locusts?"

"What right have we got to hog all the food?"

"We grew it, didn't we?"

"Yes – but they were working too. The city people were working producing the things we need. Why are we so special – so that we should live and they should starve?"

"If they swarm in here we'll all starve – we and them together. They'll eat everything. Milking cows, breeding sows, seed corn, the lot. Next year there'll be nothing for anybody – we'll all starve. At least if the farmers keep alive we can go on growing food and be able to feed somebody."

"There should be enough food in this country for everybody and for seed corn and the rest of it too."

"Yes, well there isn't. Ever since I've been in farming successive governments have had a cheap food policy. Food in England has always been cheaper than anywhere else in Europe. Whatever else was stopped by tariffs, food never was. The Dutch, the French, the Spanish and Italians – anybody in the world – was allowed to dump food into this country, subsidised like hell by their governments. Yet manufactured goods – the machinery and other things we farmers need to grow our food – were heavily protected. To hell with the city people! They screwed us when they had the chance – now we'll screw them for a change."

"Bob! You can't talk like that! I would never have believed it possible that you of all people could come out with that crap. You're a bloody fascist!"

"I'm not a fascist! I just want to save your life – and the kids and me too – and I want to save Cragpit Farm so that it can go on growing food for people to eat. Tell you what. I told old Dugdale yesterday that I'd join his territorials – and I will too. We'll keep the city hordes out of our area."

I was so disgusted about the whole thing – the whole attitude of "Fuck you, I'm all right!" – that I got together with some others and called a meeting down at the Town Hall. Both Bob and I went to that meeting. It shows something of the way we felt about each other that we walked there separately. Bob called me and said that he was going and I made an excuse, then walked across the fields instead. It was the first time we had ever really had a row.

At the meeting I could see that Bob wanted to make amends, a bit at least. He sheepishly came and sat beside me. I didn't look at him. I got up and said:

"I put it to the people of Gretford that it is our duty, as living in a food-producing district, to feed as many of the starving people of England as possible."

There were cries of "hear, hear!" and boos, and two or three people got up to shout at once. Finally Lady Mary, Sir Reginald's old terror of a wife, strode up to the empty platform, banged on the table with a hammer, and boomed: "Does anybody want me to chair this meeting? Then we can get on with it instead of all shouting at one another!"

We all shouted "yes" and she managed in some miraculous way to shut us all up. Then, to my surprise and delight, my Bob got up. At first I thought he was going to do his "F-you" act but not a bit of it. I will try to remember what he said:

"It is no good us letting millions of people swarm across the Gret and the Mudde. We are farmers here and we cannot farm if we are overrun with starving people. We must keep this bit of England clear until things return to normal. But we must tighten our belts ourselves - we must not be living in plenty while others starve. We must ration the people of this district very strictly and spare every ounce of food that we have got for the people in the rest of England. But we must not allow ourselves to be overwhelmed by the rest of England. We must stop the hordes at the bridges - for mark me the hordes will come. They haven't begun to arrive yet but they will come."

"Will we turn back women and starving orphans?" demanded a woman. "What are you talking about?"

It was a hot and acrimonious argument. I imagine the same argument was going on in many another part of rural England. One thing that was very obvious from this discussion was that only a tiny handful of us, in this very rural part of England, had anything to do with the land at all.

In the end it was moved that we should work out just how many people we could allow in over the rivers; these people should be allowed in and billeted on people, or accommodated in various large buildings, they should be fed, and that meanwhile we should be ready, as soon as transport was available, to send away as much food as could be spared to the cities. I don't know whether this meeting achieved anything, but at least some of us felt a lot better after it.

We were unique at Cragpit Farm in having some horses. Working horses that is – lots of people had hobby-horses, ponies for their little girls or showjumpers or things like that. But we had, besides Jean's pony, Golden, and my hunter, Jack, two Suffolk Punches – a mare and a gelding. Bob used these two horses quite often for various jobs about the farm. No doubt it was uneconomic, but neither Bob nor I were economists. Bob used to say it was the economists who had got the world into the state it had got in. He called economics "the dismal science".

During the cold winter we couldn't work on the land anyway, because it was under snow and frozen up. But Bob made a sled and he spent every day out in the woods with a chainsaw when he wasn't sledding the timber out or carting it down to Gretford to distribute it to people who needed it. There was plenty to eat in the District – absolutely no shortage at all. We had fifty tons of spuds, for example, and plenty of grain. As for milk and meat – both we and London Farming would willingly have sent plenty of it to the rest of England, but there was no way of getting it there and no transport anyway. London Farming had a big oil store but we weren't so fortunate. We began to wonder what we would do for haysel and harvest. We could do a lot with the horses but not everything, and we had no horse-drawn grass mower or horse-drawn reaper-and-binder, although we had a motorised one. Our worries were allayed by Mick Miller who sailed his barge up our river and tied her to the old farm quay. He brought us diesel. We hauled the diesel out, carefully hid half of it under the straw in the barn and handed the rest of it over to Major Dugdale for his comedy army.

We saw other ships out at sea occasionally. We watched a Belgian trawler once, scraping fish up just off-shore. I suppose her skipper knew that no fisheries protection vessel was going out to stop him. The odd collier went past until about the end of February then we noticed that they came no more. I used to look out to sea sometimes and think – this is what it was like before men moved on the Earth. The world seemed so peaceful.

Bob began breaking oxen in to the yoke. He made the yokes

from ash – he'd seen yoked oxen in Africa somewhere and knew how to do it. It was great fun, real wild-west at first.

I remember once having a visit from Clifford Brown, that horrible man, and Major Dugdale one day. We stood in a field watching Dickie, a boy who worked for us, driving a span of ten oxen in front of a big old-fashioned three-furrow plough that we had, with Robin leading the front pair of beasts – the toe-laier Bob called him.

"My God, Hurlock – do you really think it will come to this?" asked Dugdale.

"Damned sure it will," said Bob. "I would have thought any fool could see that simple fact. And the sooner London Farming gets busy breaking in some of those black-and-white water pumps you've got, the better for us all."

"I'm sure oil supplies will be regularised again very soon," said Brown. "After all – there's still plenty of oil in Mexico and in the Arctic too."

"Mexico is a hell of a long way from here," said Bob.

"So's the Arctic." Dugdale had more sense than his companion.

"I think it's an idea worth considering," he said.

Neither Bob nor I took much interest in local politics, but one day politics came to us.

Chapter Three

by Captain Mick Miller
(Master of the Sailing Barge *Suffolkman)*

(Recorded by Eliza Keeble)

When I heard the Prime Minister's speech I was sitting in my Day Room aboard the tanker *Orion* of which I was Master, and we were loaded with forty-thousand tonnes of crude oil bound for Filey, having loaded from a platform in the Rockall Field. We were about level with Orfordness at the time, but well outside of everything. I remember how cold it was, for the seas that we were taking over the side – there was a fresh easterly blowing – froze as they hit the deck.

I remember being vaguely interested and excited and thinking that at least we would be doing the most useful job in the country, for if anybody could keep things going, it was us, and that at least the strike of refinery workers, and dockers, that we had heard was on in Southampton Water, would not be on now. Martial Law! Let the skiving dockers sort that one out. I was worried about our engines. The Chief was continually moaning about spare parts and saying that if we didn't have a major refit we would be in trouble. The fact was it was getting harder and harder to keep ships going at all. The parts were simply not available and constant industrial trouble in the dockyards was making things more and more difficult. I sometimes thought what a pity there had to be any landlubbers at all, except farmers.

They did a good job. I remember saying once to a mate of mine: "Half the people ashore's useless," and he answered "yes - dam' nigh as useless as the other half!" We sailors were all right - we slogged about the oceans in fair weather and foul but we didn't get the back-up from the shore people. Ashore it was all strikes and scrounging and people living off the State and layabouts and nonsense.

Well I could hear all was not right with the engines: a few cylinders missing, I believe, because we couldn't get new fuel pumps and injectors. I was glad when we rounded the East Goodwin. At least if the engines conked out we wouldn't be off a lee shore. We got into the Solent only to hear that all the berths were taken and we had to anchor.

This annoyed us. The cook was running short of stores, and the crew were out of tobacco because there had been a shortage of the stuff for some time then, and if you've ever been shipmates with a tobacco-less crew you'll know what that meant. Fortunately for me I don't use the stuff. From what I could make out from the radio, the refinery had been taken over by the Navy. But the Navy didn't particularly know how to operate it, the refinery workers refused to work without food and there wasn't any food, and they had all decamped to look for some and the tankers alongside couldn't discharge and it was all a big balls-up. It struck me that there was something really insane if the English people, in this hour of emergency, could not keep the one thing that could have saved them going - the oil. But then, of course, I was later to realise that it wasn't the oil that was the real problem - it was the grub. You can't eat oil.

Anyway a boat came out from Portsmouth - we were anchored at Spithead - with some naval chaps, and they came aboard with orders for us to turn round and take our load to the Isle of Grain, in Kent, up the Medway. I refused to go unless we were supplied with victuals and baccy. I was worried about the engines anyway, and there was an easterly gale blowing.

They went ashore and came out with what we required in the grub line, and even a few bottles of whisky and some tobacco (whoever else went short, the Navy didn't). We waited two days for the gale to go down – it veered south-easterly – then we up-anchored and steamed for the Medway.

We got there all right and found things better there – the refinery was still working, under military supervision, and we managed to discharge. Then the Chief came to me and said "no go". He refused to restart the engines until they had been attended to. He was quite right too.

So there we lay tied up to the jetty and nothing would make us shift. By then the telephones weren't working, I couldn't get in touch with the Company, I couldn't find an engineering firm, I didn't know what the hell to do. I had been brought up in sailing barges – that dates me I suppose! – and in one of those things if anything went wrong you could mend it yourself with a hammer and a few nails or a sail-maker's needle. In a modern ship there is nothing you can do. If the people ashore can't help you when something goes wrong you are stuck.

Orion was an old tanker. We were due for a Board of Trade survey and a major refit anyway. I wondered what the hell to do. One by one the crew drifted off and left me. Finally there was me, the Chief, who was a Scotsman and wasn't going to leave the ship while we still had a tot of that whisky, the steward and a couple of deckhands. I gave the others permission to go – provided they got in touch again in a week. We had run out of grub again, you see. I went ashore and raised hell with the Army, and they gave us a sack of wheat of all things – what the hell were we going to do with a sack of wheat? – and a sheep carcase that hadn't even been cut up. I soon cut it up though and then they brought us a few spuds so at least we could have spuds and mutton.

There were other loaded tankers outside and they wanted our berth. But I refused to move the ship with the crew we had. So they sent for the Navy. A naval party came aboard, and very nice chaps they were, and together we moved the ship – they even had a couple of tugs which they commandeered. They moored us up fore and aft off Queenborough.

"And what the hell am I supposed to do?" I asked them. I told them I wanted to go to London to the head office of our company in Fenchurch Street.

They said that they had a launch going up that way next morning, with some top brass aboard, and I could have a lift in her. So off we went next morning, up London River, tied up at the jetty by the Tower, and I went ashore. They told me they would be going back that afternoon – they were going on up to Westminster.

Well the place was in chaos. The City was empty – except for gangs of louts breaking into restaurants and food shops to try to find food I suppose. There were some soldiers guarding the Bank of England, though what the hell for I couldn't fathom – there was nothing you could eat in there. I walked to Fenchurch Street; there was no traffic except the odd armoured car, and then there was nothing. The head office of the company had been broken into; there was nobody there, only disorder. I remember foolishly picking up a phone and it didn't buzz. That was the first time I really felt that something really dreadful had happened to the world. I just didn't know what to do. I felt helpless.

I went back to the jetty again and waited till the launch returned. There was this Admiral aboard. He was a nice chap and I asked him what the hell I should do. "Stick to your ship," he replied. "What else can you do?"

"But what's the good of that. The ship won't go!"

"Look – none of us know what to do. They tell me I must help the civil power – but where is the civil power? I can't find any. I just can't advise you my friend. Have another tot. I even went up to the Houses of Parliament – and had lunch there in the Lords' restaurant – they aren't short of food yet – but just nobody knows what to do. We had a conference at the Admiralty and the First Sea Lord said that we at Chatham were to administer East Kent in conjunction with the military. So that's what I suppose we'll do. If you want to come and join us – you're a sailor – I daresay we could take you on. But you'd better stand by your ship for a week or two anyway. Maybe things will return to normal and you can get your engine repaired."

But when I thought of that empty, looted, office I had little hope of getting any engine repairs.

Anyway the Chief and I stayed aboard the ship. We put a boat in the water and used to go over to Sheerness occasionally and the Navy would give us odds and ends of grub. The Chief worked on the engines and found all sorts of things wrong with them – new parts were needed – and neither of us really knew what the hell to do. We used to listen to the radio – shipping band of course – and the picture we got was one of mounting chaos. Tankers were going up to the oil platforms and finding nobody there to serve them – the people on the rigs had gone ashore because there was no grub for them. Astonishing, really, that the people ashore didn't seem to have the sense to find grub to spare for the one lot of people who could have kept things going – but then, I suppose, it was a complete breakdown in communications and morale. Ashore the system that should have been getting refined products away from the refineries had broken down too and the refineries couldn't take in any more crude. The Isle of Grain went like that.

The big power station on Grain went on knocking out power and ashore all the lights were on, until about a week after we berthed off Queenborough, and then – bang. The Chief and I were sitting in the Day Room having an evening tot and the Chief suddenly said "Mick – the lights have gone out!" Ashore there was nothing, only blackness, except where the oil flares at the refinery were still lighting up the sky.

We finished the whisky that night, and the Navy wouldn't give us any more. The Chief said he thought he'd go ashore. Like me he wasn't married but he had friends up at Greenhithe and thought he'd go and try his luck there. I advised him not to go so near London but he knew best. He showed me how to work the auxiliary engine that produced our electricity. I think it was at that moment I decided to leave the ship myself. I couldn't see any point in staying aboard any longer.

Next day was a cold, bright day with a fresh north-easterly

wind. I remember walking out, after I had had some sort of breakfast, on to the main deck and striding up and down to get some exercise and wondering what the hell to do. I remember thinking how ugly everything aboard a modern ship was! I thought back to my early days aboard the sailing barge and remembered how beautiful those sailing barges were. Sailing ships generally in fact. I'm not talking about modern yachts built of Tupperware but real wood-built working vessels. There was something magnificent about them.

And just then – blow me down – what should I see but the old familiar shape just coming clear of the point! There she was, on the starboard tack – a real live sailing barge. Even at that distance I could see she wasn't being sailed by a bargeman – how could she be? – there were hardly any of us left. She wasn't pointing very well, her mainsail looked like a sack and her topsail was set about as well as a Dutchman's trousers.

She made several tacks – dam' nearly missed stays every time – then came straight for my ship on the port tack – falling away to leeward like a wash tub. I just stood and watched her and I really was shocked and distressed at the way she was being handled.

You see when I first went to sea – I ran away at the age of thirteen and that was in 1950 I suppose, at least after the end of the War – there were hundreds of East Coast sailing barges. They were the finest craft ever built anywhere. The small ones, like the one I was watching, could carry a hundred and thirty tons of cargo and be sailed by a man and a boy. They went anywhere in the North Sea. A couple even crossed the Atlantic once. They were sold in South America. In both the world wars a lot of them sailed down to Scapa Flow, to tender for the Navy. The men who sailed them were a race apart. We looked upon ourselves as entirely different from anybody else – we knew that what we were doing nobody else could do, for it was perhaps the toughest job you could do anywhere, ashore or afloat.

Then gradually, after the Hitler War, the thing fell apart. It wasn't so much the motor ships that knocked us out – it was the road transport. Nothing could compete against the road. Nothing.

The railways only survived because the Government subsidised them. And one by one the old barges were laid up and most of them were sold to yachties. The yachties bought them, kept some of them going, and sailed others onto the sands and lost them. Some managed to hire old bargemen to show them the ropes – they must have had tons of money just to keep the barges going at all. And here sailing towards me was the old *Suffolkman*. I remembered her when old Bert Quantrill was her skipper and a good old barge she was too. When I say "yachties sailed them", they didn't trade with them of course. They sailed them for fun or else, like the *Suffolkman* they fitted them out with bunks and hammocks in the hold and took people cruising for pleasure at so much a week. A lot of the old bargemen hated to see these fine old ships in the hands of yachties who hadn't the faintest idea really how to sail them. I always thought myself it was better to see them kept going and, in the case of the *Suffolkman* how right I was.

And there she came – sagging away to leeward on the port tack – fetching across straight to the *Orion's* upstream moorings. It was typical of a yachty that the man who was steering her couldn't see for himself that she had too much draught to clear my mooring wires – which were under water where she would come across. The tide was ebbing fast and I could see real trouble coming.

I walked aft and cupped my hands and yelled: "You're sailing straight into my moorings! Up-helm and bear away!" And when he did seem to understand I yelled: "Turn your wheel to starboard and bear off or you'll sail straight into my moorings."

At last he understood and he bore away – the old barge heeled right over when she came beam-on to the wind because he didn't think to let go some mainsheet – and she just missed the mooring buoy by a fathom or two. She was then sailing straight for the mud. He brought her up into the wind again, brought her too far and her sails came ashake, she fell off again and sailed straight onto the mud.

There were several people aboard, including some girls, and

they all began to run around in a panic. The tide was taking off fast of course and I knew they would not get off that tide at least. After a lot of gafuffle they managed to get the canvas off her. And there she sat – hard and fast on the putty.

Having nothing better to do I decided to go aboard. I jumped into the boat that we had been using for our shore trips and sculled over to the barge. There was still enough water round her for me to float. I climbed aboard.

Her skipper seemed a bit sheepish. "She wouldn't answer the helm!" he said.

"No, I bet she wouldn't seeing that you put it the wrong way," I said.

Well, to cut a long story short, I found they all lived aboard this barge and sometimes an old bargeman, who I used to know, called Bill Rands used to come and join them and they would take part in these barge races these yachties used to have. They had been lying at Hoo, with a number of other yacht-barges, when the Navy had come along to tell them that the barges were to be requisitioned. It seems that someone in the Navy had had the sense to see that this would be a good idea – in case the oil finally did run out. This lot had decided they didn't want to be requisitioned and so they had set sail and dropped down-stream intending to sail for Maldon in Essex where they all came from.

"You're not going to get to Maldon like this," I told them. "In fact you're bloody lucky to have got as far as you have got. If it hadn't been for this hot ebb-tide you would never have made it against this wind at all. This barge is sailing like a bath-tub."

"We began to realise we weren't doing all that well," said the skipper, whose name, by the way, was Mike Wrinch. "What do you think we were doing wrong?"

I had a job to think what they were doing right.

"Have you got any grub aboard?" I said.

They had, and plenty of it too.

"Give me a good meal first and then I'll sort this lot out for you," I said. After dinner I lowered the mast and shortened the stanliff so as to take some of the slack out of the mainsail. We hoisted the gear again and managed to flatten out the topsail by some adjustments to the clew outhaul and the halyard. We hove down on the stay-fall tackle so as to spring the top mast forward. The gear was all good – brand new in fact. I couldn't help remembering the old days of real barging when we used to have to slog up and down the coast in fair weather and foul with our gear all to pieces because we couldn't afford to renew it. It seemed wrong that these yachties, who only sailed in fair weather in summer time, should be able to reeve brand new nylon ropes and set new terylene canvas. And they did it just for pleasure when we had had to earn a living.

After a couple more ebbs had gone by I reckoned the barge was fit to sail.

"High water'll be at ten tomorrow," I said. "You'd better get away then before the Navy comes and nabs you." The wind was still north-easterly.

"You wouldn't like to come with us Skip?" said one of the girls.

Well I thought about it. After all – what was the good of being a master of a forty-thousand tonne tanker which wouldn't go? I looked out at that huge grey wall of steel lying to two moorings and thought what a useless great ugly object it was.

I liked the girls. As for Mike I realised he wouldn't make a sailor as long as he had a hole in his arse.

I thought – well I might as well go with them as far as Maldon. They had plenty of grub on board.

To cut, again, a long story short I decided to sail with them as far as Maldon.

At nine next day we mustered and let go the brails to set the mainsail and hauled up the topsail. As the flood slackened we hove in the anchor cable. At slack tide we had the anchor, the girls hove up the foresail and backed it to starboard, we fell away on the starboard tack.

She gathered way nicely. I bore away and cleared the *Orion's* upstream mooring, hauled her on the wind again and she cut up to windward like a good 'un. I realised what a good barge she was. I longed to see how she would go to windward with a freight in her hold.

We beat all the way to the Spitway (that's a gut between the Buxey Sand and the Gunfleet) and we just saved our ebb over it – our leeboard bumping on the sand as we went through. It all came back to me. I hadn't sailed through the Spitway for, well since 1955 when I left sailing barges for good (they left me – that was just about the end of 'em) but it all came back to me. Funny – I knew exactly how much water we would have through the Spitway, I could have gauged that within an inch.

Once through the Spitway we put her over on the starboard tack again and raced up into the Blackwater with a spanking wind on her quarter. She went like hell! It was lovely. I realised that this was the life I was cut out for – not standing about in some stuffy air-conditioned control room looking at dials and pressing buttons! This was fun!

I remember one of those pretty girls coming to me with a mug of cocoa.

"Captain you've been at that wheel for six hours," she said. "Wouldn't you like a rest?"

"It's a soldier's wind – you have a go!" I said, and I tried to teach her how to steer.

We sailed her alongside the Maldon Quay, made her fast, and got the sails off her. I'll never forget – the old barge looked pleased somehow! She looked as if she'd enjoyed herself. I felt I just wanted to see a full cargo lowered down into her belly and help her make a good voyage then. Then she'd have something to be pleased about and so would I!

Well, things moved quite fast. Mike Wrinch, I found, didn't own the barge – she belonged to the father of the two girls, who were sisters, Meg and Jane. Their father lived at Maldon. They had allowed Mike to come aboard because he was a yachtie and thought he knew all about navigation. The two girls asked me to ship aboard as full-time skipper – and they would be the crew. I'd never dreamt of an all-girl crew before but why not? I thought. They both looked to me as if they would shape up. I'd sailed a barge with one boy for a mate many a time and decided these two lassies would make up one boy together. As it turned out they were as good as a dozen boys. They've proved marvellous and I don't mind who knows it.

The father – Jimmy Warner his name was – owned a mill in Maldon and was a corn merchant and a few things like that. He suggested to me that we should trade with the barge and try to make what living we could under the altered circumstances. He had an idea that, all normal means of transport having broken down, if we bought wheat in the country and sold it in London we would help people survive and survive ourselves. He hadn't reckoned on how things had gone.

There was no wheat near Maldon, it had all been confiscated by the Army.

"Try further down the coast," he said. Or rather I suppose he said up the coast being a landlubber – we sailormen always said down north and up south in the North Sea. The tide goes that way. I decided to go to an old haunt of mine: Gretford, in Suffolk.

Gretford was far from London – and far from Birmingham and the Midland cities too. I decided that we would have as good a chance of loading some wheat or other produce there as anywhere.

We both realised of course that money wouldn't be much good to buy it with. The one thing we knew we could use as a medium of exchange was oil. Oil and petrol in fact. Well Jimmy had a finger in many pies and he knew where he could get some drums that had held chemicals and I had seen a John Harker tanker, a little coaster tanker, lying off Bradwell in the Blackwater which didn't seem to have any crew in her. So we loaded these empty drums, sailed down the Blackwater and came alongside this tanker. She was deserted, and it didn't take me long to bring a hose into the barge and load a couple of thousand gallons of diesel, which is what she was carrying. I don't think anybody saw us, from the shore or anywhere else.

Then we let go and sailed down-Swin for the River Gret, or

Gretford River as we bargemen call it. The wind had veered south-westerly, I remember, and we roared down-Swin and reached straight in to the river on the last of the flood – we had been stemming the tide outside – and sailed up that river like a dream.

I don't know what made me do it but I sailed her straight past Gretford Quay. I went on a mile or two until I saw this farm with some haystacks and corn ricks in the yard. Most unusual sight in those days. So we lot stopped there and went ashore in the boat – I and my two fair crew mates – to go and see if we could strike a bargain.

Chapter Four

by Bob Hurlock

I was out in the yard sawing logs. It was about mid-February. Still felt I had enough fuel to run the tractor-mounted circular saw. Jessie and the kids were helping by bringing the trunks to me and carrying the cut logs away to put in the trailer to take down to town. It was still deep snow and bloody cold.

I saw three men approaching.

Down we sat, with some two year-old elderberry wine.

"Go to hell thass a drop o' good," said Dike, who was doing all the talking. "Have you tried that muck London Farming have been brewing?"

"No I haven't."

He compared it to some unmentionable liquid. "You ought to make your own beer together," he said. "My mother always brewed."

"So did mine," said Harry Blendover.

"Well you'd better get on and do it too," I said.

There was a pause.

"What we want to see you about Bob," started Dike, "is – will you join our party and contest this election they're having in April?"

I had heard that an election had been fixed for the First of April, April Fool's Day, for a council of five men to govern our little pocket of England.

"I'm no bloody politician," I said.

"Listen," said Dike. "There's this bunch of fools we got now – who want to keep London Farming as the be-all and end-all and us all work for it and not ourselves. Then there's another party – the Bible-bashers. The Baptists and Congregationalists and Methodists and all that lot. They've sunk their differences and are putting up candidates although what their programme is the Lord alone knows. Back to God and all that – but that isn't going to feed us. But several of us round about want to form a third party. And we want you to lead it."

"Why me of all people?"

"Because you're about the only independent man – independent farmer – left. We know there's one or two others, but they couldn't lead a party."

"What do you want to do?"

"Split the land up into small holdings and let each man have his share. That's what."

I thought for a bit. Then I said: "Look, when I got up at that church meeting and suggested splitting the cows up – all I got was a silly laugh. Not one of you together got up and said he agreed with me. No-one spoke up then. You can stew in your own juice."

"So it's dam' you I'm all right?" said Bill Smithers.

"Well – no not exactly that. I'd help you if I could. But what's wrong with the way things are going now?"

"What's wrong?" said Dike. "Everything's wrong. All those pip-squeaks of managers and under-managers, and efficiency experts, and clerks sitting in the office, lording it over us and what the hell do they know about farming? And another thing – the oil's finished. What about that? What's London Farming going to do about that?"

"Well what are you going to do?"

"Look – you know dam' well – a good man on five or ten acres can grow a hell of a lot of good food. Without oil. That's what we want. A good man on five or ten or twenty acres – we could train oxen like you've done come to that – we could keep a cow or two – fatten pigs – grow what we need. We'd be men again instead of just bits of a machine. And the land'd produce ten times as much. And London Farming say they own it – who are London Farming? Head office in London – there is no London. It don't belong to Brown – who the hell does it belong to? Let's divide the land out as fairly as we can, to people who know how to use it, and then go on from there. That's what we say. And we want to contest this election."

"Why don't you stand?" I said to Dike.

"I'm not a lettered man," said Dike. "That want someone who can spout a bit."

"What are you going to call it?"

"Don't matter what the hell we call it. So it gets in."

"Well what about . . . Land Reform Party?"

"Fair enough." The other two agreed.

"You've got to help us Bob," said Dike. "You've no idea what a mess and a muddle they're getting into up there. They'll get no spring wheat in – not a stetch. The winter wheat's been killed. They've got to plant their spuds by hand – but they can't get nobody to do na work. They can't get the cows milked – nine-tenths of 'em dried-off already. Half of 'em got mastitis. They – the people – can't get milk for the kiddies even. They keep a'grinding wheat – but that's going to dry up soon. They got to keep some oil for emergencies. It's all a mess. He keep saying, "If only we could get more diesel for the tractors!" Well yes – silly fool – everything would be easy then but we can't so there's an end to it. If we could get into this here council and shove those buggers out – I don't want to be a councillor – none of us do – but we can see that we'll all starve next year if something ain't done. We want to share this land out so's we can all get to work and pull it about a bit and get some spring wheat in, and keep a cow or two so's we can get some milk and rear up a few head of stock. We'll all starve else – do you see."

"There's another thing – pigs," said Bill Smithers, who was a pigman up at London Farming. "They can't get any of this here swine fever vaccine. Now they got four hundred sows all in one building – what's going to happen if swine fever hits 'em? Or swine vesicular disease? or erysipelas? We shan't have a pig left alive. What are we going to eat? Them pigs ought to be distributed out so's they're-scattered about – a few here and a few there."

"You are right," I said. "I know dam' well you are. I've been thinking the same thing long before the Crash. But why don't you stand yourselves?"

"Because we aren't a'gooin' to," said Harry. "We in't scholards enough. They want a man what can read and write and spout a bit. You think about it, and don't think too long – do that'll be too late."

And, laden with eggs (which neither they nor their families had eaten since fowl-pest had swept though the enormous hen battery house of London Farming) they took their leave.

The next day a boy on a bicycle brought me a note from Dike asking me if I could meet him, and a few others, at *The Barge Inn*, which was a public house at a place called Yeldham Ferry. Accordingly, I set out after tea that afternoon on my horse. (When I say "tea" I mean the meal we ate at half past four in the afternoon. Anyone who reads this book will remember the fearful headaches and bad temper we all suffered as we had to train our bodies to do without caffeine.)

Yeldham Ferry was a scattered hamlet five miles to the north of our farm, on the bank of the River Gret. No ferry operated there then, but at the point where the ferry had once docked stood *The Barge*. My way led straight from my own farm into Forestry Commission land, and from there on the bridle path, which I followed, was hemmed on both sides by Scots and Corsican pine trees. The pine forest came right to the bank of the river, and *The Barge Inn* stood in a clearing. There were several Forestry Commission-owned small holdings about there: places left unplanted in the forest which were let to private individuals who had to spend so many days a year working for the Commission and could spend the rest working for themselves. Yeldham Ferry was a very remote spot. The road that ran past it ran nowhere in particular. There was very little traffic and very few strangers particular. There was very little traffic and very few strangers ever went there, even in that period when every man-jack of us had a car and leisure to drive about in it. Thus something of the spirit of Old England still remained there. People still sang songs in the pub, and played the melodeon, and conversed in broadest Suffolk. Once the brewers installed a thing called a jukebox (a hideous instrument for reproducing terrible music) the customers carried the thing out one night and dumped it in the Gret. I liked it at *The Barge* and often, in the days gone by, used to ride through the forest on my horse and spend many an evening there.

On this occasion I rode into the clearing and saw the little flint building that was the Inn, rode round the back of it and tied Duke in the stable (he was the only horse who ever got put there) and went in through the back door.

To my surprise everybody was drinking beer.

"Come on Captain – have a pint of Mother Denny's Best!" shouted someone, and thrust a pint mug in my hands. The beer in it was darkish, sweetish, but very pleasant. I realised it was home-brewed. Mrs Denny, the landlady of *The Barge*, had evidently got to work.

An indignation meeting was going on.

The Back To God Party, as the party of the nonconformist church groups had named itself, had announced that if they were elected the first thing they would do would be to ban all use of intoxicating liquors.

"They're worse than the blasted nobs!" somebody was saying. "Old Sir Charles will at least stand you a drink if he happen in the pub. He's a good ol' boy he is – he stood me a double whisky last time he come in here. He asked me what I'd have, I say a whisky, he say 'make it a double, Mrs Denny!'"

"Yes but why should he reckon he have all the shooting on London Farming land?" said a man named Bill Worledge. "He and Brown? Tell me that? And who owns the pheasants and the wild birds now? And what about this here syndicate of gents what own the shooting on Forestry land? Where are they now? Starved to dead I doubt. And yet old Ross still think he can keep anyone from taking a bird now and again if they want one. It's all wrong to my way of thinking."

"Well here's Captain Hurlock," said Bill Smithers. "Tell him what you want to say to him together."

There was a silence among the twenty-odd men who crowded the little, tobacco-smoke-stained room, and then a man named Eli Woolpit spoke up. Eli was an old friend of mine too. The Woolpits were a local family, but Eli's father had married a Traveller, or Gypsy woman, and Eli had many Traveller characteristics. True his hair was red, and not black, but he had the Traveller's love of dogs (particularly "long dogs" or lurchers), of horses, singing and step-dancing, music and sometimes even fighting. He was flamboyant, and wore gold earrings and a bright red neckerchief. People either liked him or were afraid of him. He was highly intelligent, although it was rumoured that he could neither read or write. He was tall, thin-faced with long side-boards, and he looked very distinguished, in his way. Forty-five-ish, he drove a lorry for the Forestry, but did a lot of dealing on the side. He used to come to my farm sometimes and buy scrap, or old hens, or anything that I would sell him as he put it – "wu'th the money".

"Look here Cap'n Robert," said Eli. "We want you to head this party what Dike and them has got up. He call that the Land Reform Party he do – he'll tell you all about it himself. He in't come in yet. We all reckon you're the man for the job. You're the biggest independent farmer here about – you're the only one come to that. And you're educated – you can spout. If them Bible-bashers get in we shan't be allowed a drink even – and if them London Farming lot get in again we shall all starve to dead. I in't no farmer but that don't take a genius to make that out. If we each had our own little piece of land we could scratch about and grow something regardless of tractor oil. If the cows and pigs and things was distributed round we could feed 'em off our own bits of land and keep a'gooin'. That seems simple enough to me – thass as clear as gin."

"Good ol' boy!" shouted somebody. "Give him a pint of

Mother Denny's Special. He'll be Prime Minister yet."

Eli was given a pint of Mother Denny's Special. I was given another. There was no trouble about paying for this beverage: London Farming had printed their own currency, and issued everybody who applied for it with fifty of their pounds every Friday. As most of the produce which people could buy came from London Farming they got it all back and the system worked quite well. Mrs Denny had bought her barley from London Farming, to make the malt to brew her excellent beer. There was beer to spare for everybody.

I had to say something. So I said, from my place leaning up at the end of the bar: "Well I agree with you – every word you say. But why drag me in? What about you and Dike and the rest of you having a go? I don't want to be any damned prime minister. I wanta- worka-da-mine!"

"They want somebody with a bit of a head on him to be chairman," said Bill Smithers. "People won't vote for just we chaps. That want someone like yourself to head it to get people to vote."

Dike came in at that juncture. "Come on Dike!" I said. "They want you to be President!"

"Well they got another think coming," said Dike. He then went on to explain that there were five seats to be fought at the coming election: One for each of the parishes in our little district of country that had been spared. They wanted me to stand for Shoreness, where my farm lay, he would stand for Gretford, Eli for Yeldham Ferry, Bill Smithers for Sibford, and a young fellow who had just finished three years at Exeter University where he had read Geology would stand for Muddebridge.

Well, we all agreed to do this, although I agreed to taking part myself reluctantly. But I did agree, because I thought the issue was important. I could see a real breakdown in food supplies and everything else if our party did not get in. A huge organisation like London Farming could never adapt itself to a world of hand, horse and ox labour. We would have to get back to a peasant economy, and quickly, if we were to survive. Either that or some

sort of feudal or slave system would develop with a few grand
Seigneurs, and I could not see people like Eli Woolpit and Dike
Randle fitting into that. And after we had finished the political
business a man named Fred started up *Pigeon on a Gate* on the
melodeon, Eli got up and step-danced until the sweat ran down
his face, his little wife Mary got up and danced opposite him.
Dike then sang: *The Dark-Eyed Sailor*, an old, old man got up
and sang *The Bonnie Bunch of Roses Oh!* in a croaky voice, and
a young man with oily hair treated us to some American number
about his "babby", who wasn't "treoo", and this made him
"bleoo". It was that sort of pub.

Well, next day the election campaign began in earnest. Nobody
seemed to take the Land Reform party seriously. We aroused
good-natured amusement, and that seemed to be that. A few
people, mostly the older farm workers but also a few younger
men, came up and said they agreed with us and would give us
their votes, but for the most we were listened to with amusement
and then politely ignored.

Not so the other two parties. The Conservatives, under Sir
Charles Lloyd, had the whole-hearted allegiance of all the Church
of England people. The Back To God Party, of course, had the
allegiance of the chapelgoers. These two parties spent so much
time attacking each other that they seemed to forget all about us.
There were no deposits to be laid down by candidates, which I
felt was just as well, for if there had have been I was quite sure
that our party would be five deposits down.

Well, we travelled around, mostly on bicycles; we held
meetings and gave speeches. The Land Reformers were very
inconspicuous, but the chapelgoers held large open-air rallies,
sang hymns, had the Salvation Army march about beating drums
and playing instruments, and the Conservatives sang *Land of
Hope and Glory*, issued free beer, had big meetings, and the
vicar of Gretford delivered political sermons in his church.

And the election was held.

The Land Reform Party simply romped in. We won all five
seats: there was no opposition.

Chapter Five

by Dike Randle

(recorded by Eliza Keeble)
(Note by Eliza: I have tried to write down Dike's lovely Suffolk
accent as well as I can. Hope I've got the spelling right.)

Well I don' know why you together want me to tell this tale –
every one of you's more lettered than I am. And it weren't me
that was Prime Minister. It was Jessie mostly what insisted that it
should be we ordinary working men on the Council. All I wanted
to do was to get a bit of ground and dig it and grow some taters.
But – like a lot of good things – it all come to nothing in the end.

After this here election old Gurling and "Save-Soul" Jones
came up to Bob and me and says: "We'll help you all we can to
keep the place a'running. As for dividing up the land that might
not be a bad idea either." The other lot – the Conservatives – had
different ideas. They weren't a'going to have it if they could help
it. Ol' Sir Charles surprised us though. He come up and say that
he reckon that some – purely temporary – redistribution of the
land were necessary. But he says he know London Farming still
had quite a bit of oil up their sleeve. Enough to get the spring
seed in anyway. But he reckon Clifford Brown would never hear
of any distribution. He wouldn't let goo of an inch of London
Farming land do he could keep his mitts on it.

I remember I asked Sir Charles do he'd help me on some sort
of board we was going to set up to redistribute the land. "Yes,

yes," he say. "I sarved on the conchie board during the war didn't I? And I bin on the bench enough years."

So he and me went along to Clifford Brown's London Farming offices. Me having been chosen as Minister of Agriculture like.

"Mr Brown," I say. "Will you sarve on this here board to redistribute the land?"

"Most certainly not," he say. "I haven't been put in charge of London Farming land to give it away to any Tom, Dick or Harry."

"Come come!" say Sir Charles. "There's bin a free election you know. We've all got to sarve the new Council loyally. It was in their programme to distribute the land. This is a democracy you know!"

"Until the law of England is changed I shall abide by it!" he say.

"We don't want to take all London Farming land," I say. "What we've promised is to take enough land off the big owners to give every man and woman in the district a good garden. Enough what they can dig with a spade and grow some grub on. You may have some oil now – but what about next year when there in't any?"

"The oil supply will be regularised by then I am quite sure," he say. But Sir Charles was up to him. "Clifford," he say. "Thass got to happen. You'll still have far more'n you can farm, even with all that oil you got. We must distribute some land out to people so's they're in the way of being able to grow enough food for theirselves."

The upshot of it all was – we broke into Clifford's office next day with a section of the territorials. We warned him not to make a fool of himself. And we divided out some of the land – not much – we only took about fifty acres out of London Farming's two thousand – and this land was distributed out to all the people. And a hell of a job that were too. There was arguing and the devil knows what-all. But it come to it in the end. After all – they was all getting something for nothin' so they wasn't that bolshie.

And then they all set to – a'fencing and a'digging – you never saw such a carry-on. Little ol' pig sties rose up out of the ground like. There was cow sheds put up and I don't know what-all. We wanted the territorials again to distribute the pigs and cows. Clifford wouldn't let 'em goo. "Over my dead body," he say, but it didn't come to that. Anyone what we thought could look after 'em we dished out animals to. London Farming had no way of looking after 'em, see? The cows they couldn't get milked. The pigs'd have got swine fever or vesicular disease do they'd all bin left crowded in them Belsen houses without vaccine. We had to git 'em out. Besides we liberated, as you might say, some electric fences and we used the pigs' snouts to dig up a lot of land. They were far healthier out of doors and did the land good too – put the muck where it was needed.

And all the people were a'working like crazy. The snow went and the ground had dried out well by the end of March. People were a'digging and a'scratching about, and getting in seed – the whole countryside seemed to come to life. At first Clifford Brown went on strike but then when he found we was a'going to plough up the rest of London Farming land whatever he did he took over again and started giving orders and became a bloody nuisance and in the end we sacked him. It was something being Minister of Agriculture. But he was nothing but a damned nuisance. He got on everybody's nerves. My God when I sacked him he was some awk'ard. "I'll hev you for this!" he say. "You'll regret this!"

"May God send you better sense!" said Bob, who was there.

And he got on a bicycle and off he went along the road towards Randersfield and I thought – I hoop thass the last we see of you.

That warn't though. We saw him agin soon enough. One morning Bob and Sir Charles and me was busy in the London Farming office – thass where we had our Headquarters like – and outside we heard motors. We went out – that had become unusual – and there we see a motor and four big trucks full of soldiers. Not our terrier boys either – regular army soldiers. And this big staff car in front of 'em. And out of this car steps a major, a captain – and Clifford Brown. And did he look nasty! He did manage to mumble "Mornin' Sir Charles" but bugger a word he say to Bob. Nor yet to me.

Then this major come up to Bob and hold his hand out and say: "My name's Major Dobson. I've been sent to take over this area of country by the government." He tried to hev a posh accent but that didn't quite come off. He sounded Birmingham underneath it.

"What government?" I hear old Bob come out.

"Government of England. You're a bit cut off here. England's under military government now. Capital's in Birmingham. Headquarters of the Army." And a lot more of that squit.

Then blast if I didn't see old Hugh Giles! Cap'n Giles we called him. He was riding in front of one of the trucks. He jumped down and come over to us. "Hullo Dike you old fucker'," he say. (Sorry Eliza – but I know you don't mind language.) He was like that – we used to call him the swearing captain. Terrible man for language. "Hullo Bob!" he say. "Blast 'bor thass a long time since I sin you togither!" He was a real nob ol' Hugh Giles but he used to like to talk like we do – broad "silly Suffolk" as we say. He was a good ol' boy and I tell you what – he was the best man with a shot-gun I ever did see! I've sin him raking duck out of the sky at flighting time when thass bin dam' nigh pitch dark. Regular army man – in the Grenadier Guards he was. Real toff. Tons o' money and open-handed with it too. Rip-roaring sort of man but swear! Blast I never heard a man swear like him. Language! No-one took offence though – that was just the Captain's way. Salt of the Earth. He used to spend all his holidays down at Gretford – shooting in the winter and yachting in the summer and boozing all the time. And chasing women. And here he was in this Fred Karno's army.

Of course we were glad to see him but we wasn't too happy about the rest of 'em. All from the Sheers. We in Suffolk never got on too well with Sheers people (transcriber's note: "Sheers" is the way East Anglians have of saying "Shires". By this word we simply mean "the Midlands".) I didn't like the look of 'em at

all. Rum lot. As for this Major Dobson – he was the rummest of
'em all. He wun't wuth two-pennorth of cold cat-piss. Wu'th two
men short.

But we was landed with 'em.

As for Clifford Brown he stands there and comes out with a lot
of squit about we was a lot of thieves and had pinched London
Farming's land, and its animals, and all the rest of it.

"You knew that dam' well before you cleared off," I tell him.
"Anyway – what is this London Farming? You, I suppose?
You're only their dam' manager. London Farming had its office
in London you silly fule. And where's London now? The
shareholders are all starved to dead I doubt. Whoever did own it
– thass hard to tell who ever did own such things as that – that
never was a proper farm at all."

Anyway he stand there a'blusterin' and a'roarin'. Finally Giles
shut him up. "Come on!" he say in his gent voice. Sometimes he
used to talk like a proper gent, sometimes broad Suffolk. He'd
goo from one to the other. That was his way you see. "Let's go
to *The Crown*. What the hell are we standing here for. Brown –
come on. Don't start a quarrel as soon as we get here. It can all
be sorted out – we're all on the same side." And he shove his ol'
arm into Bob's and said "Come you along 'bor and pour some
liquor down your ol' throttle. Come on my dear chap – nothing
more boring than a bloody argument. Come on Dike! I bet that
thieving landlord's got some whisky hidden away. If he has we'll
shake it out of the bastard."

So Bob and me and Cap'n Giles we stalks over to *The Crown* –
and sure enough old Backhouse did find up a bottle of whisky
and that was a drop o' good I can tell you. That was just what we
was a'wantin'.

Then along come this soldier to tell us we was wanted at the
London Farming office. Well, we thought we'd better go there.
We got there to find Brown, Dobson and ol' Sir Charles a
'hammerin' away having some sort of conference.

"Hullo, Hurlock," says Dobson, as if I didn't exist. "Sit down
– we've a few things to say to you." He didn't look at me. Bob

got me a chair though afore he sat down hisself. "Now then," say this fule of a Major. "We've bin talking it over. I'm in command here – of all the country of East Suffolk south of the Blythe. What I say goes. And I'm putting Mr Brown here in charge of all farming and food in this area. He's a qualified agriculturist, as you must well know . . ."

"He know no more about farming than my cat!" I say.

"Mr – er – I forget your name – if you interrupt you'll have to go out."

"I don't rightly care if I'm out or in," I say. "But mark my words guvnor – do Brown here take away the land and stock from the people what's bin allotted it he'll rue the day. That 'on't pay him! He'll git an ash-plant a'top of his hid!"

Bob came in to pour oil on troubled waters. "Clifford – how do you intend to farm the land?"

"Ah, we've got oil now," says Clifford. "And we've even found a store of Avenge – and some Paraquat – and other chemicals. We'll be able to farm properly again thank God. And the Army are getting the whole country under control, and no doubt the chemical and oil situations will soon become regularised." I'm not much good at takin' him off but thass the way he spuk, more or less. And then he goo on to tell his plans. He was going to take all the land we'd handed out back and plough the bloody lot up into one field again.

"Even the land that people have sown?" Bob say. "You're mad Clifford."

"Maybe I am but that's the way it's going to be," he say. "We won't be a'needing of your services," he say. "You'd better goo back and run your own farm properly." He didn't even bother to sack me. He treated me as if I warn't there. I'll git even with this Charlie-boy afore I die! I says to meself.

And then he talk about how he didn't want a lot of peasants scratching about and we was going back to real farming. As for this "Major", he just sat there not saying a word. He didn't have a word to say. He was no more a "major" than my arse – second-hand car salesman we found he'd bin – up in the Sheers somewhere. He warn't wuth a lump of cow-dung and thass a fact.

Then in come our own Major – old Bill Dugdale. He'd bin a'sent for too.

These two majors shook hands – after Bill had saluted this other major – and he sat down.

"What happens now," says this major, "is you hand in your arms to the regular army. We'll arrange the collection", and all that squit. "Then if your chaps" he called 'em "want to do so they can apply to join the regular army." And he went on to tell us they'd be transferred away somewhere. They'd all be sent up in the Sheers somewhere.

Dam' this for a lark, thinks I. And I gits and makes for the door. They don't even see me goo I doubt – I wasn't their "class" you see. I was only a stupid peasant.

Well I might ha' bin stupid but I wasn't as stupid as some on 'em. I walks straight over to Bill Dugdale's military Land-Rover, gets in it, and drives off merrily down the square. Off I goos – waving to everybody – and they all thinks o' course I'm on territorial duty. I was in the terriers you see. And I drives off along the Randersfield road until I come to the road-block we had just afore Randersfield – that was where the lot I'd bin sergeant of was you see.

When I got there I called 'em all round me and made 'em a proper speech. "Hide your weapons," I say. "Oil 'em well, wrap 'em up in summat, and bury 'em in the pine needles in the Forestry.

They was riled this lot was. This Fred Karno's army had annoyed 'em you see. These Sheers fules had jeered at 'em and called 'em yokels and told 'em they'd got to be sent God knows where and I don't know what all. They was having an indignation meeting when I got there. Half of 'em sloped off into the woods and they was the ones that did what I told 'em. The others was scared but they was good boys and I knew they wouldn't let me down like. Do that wouldn't pay 'em and this they knew well. Some of the others go off to tell the other units to do the same.

Well, that were just as well I'd got there when I did. A few minutes after they'd dispersed – them that was going to – along comes this armoured troop carrier with a sergeant and ten men in it. "We've come to relieve you of your weapons," say this sergeant. And of course these silly fules what hadn't taken off they has to hand in their rifles but I often think they also did a good service. If they'd hidden their guns too you see the army'd have smelled a rat and hunted 'em all out again. As it was the army didn't know how many there'd bin of us. And we'd spread the word around that anyone who shopped us to the army'd get an ash plant down on his head. (Eliza's note: An ash plant is a thick walking stick made from a maiden ash tree.)

As for Major Dugdale, our gallant commander-in-chief, me and ol' Eli Woolpit went to see him. We drove up bold as brass in front of his door with his own Land-Rover. We knocks on the door and there's the major. "Can we come in Dug?" we say. "Come along in," he say. "Was it you who run off with my Land-Rover?"

"It was me Dug," I say. "I needed it on urgent business. But it's back now and none the worse and you'll be pleased about what we did in the end. Dug – we want to see the territorial record. The list of all our names and all."

"Why?" he say. "Although I don't see why you shouldn't. It's nothing special."

He brings it out.

"Thank you," I say and took it over and put it straight on his fire.

"What are you a'doing of!" he cry – and he comes to snatch it out again. Eli stand in front of him though. Eli's tall, and thick-set, and as strong as a bull. And he's known to be light tempered and easy upset. That don't do to upset him. He's had more fights than hot dinners.

So the Major doesn't rescue the roll call.

"What the hell's the idea?" he say. So we tells him what had happened. We speaks to him nicely and he sees the point I reckon. He hadn't taken to this Sheers army no more than we had. "They're a shower o' shit," he say. (Sorry Eliza, to use

language, but you tell me to say what really went on didn't you –
and I know you're not namby-pamby – I've known you since you
were right a little maather – I sin you in the bath.)

All right – I'll stick to the point. Well the major he do see the
point I reckon. We also lets him know that it might not be
healthy for him if the army got to know the names of the chaps
who'd run away. But fair play to the oud boy – I think he was on
our side really – although he never showed it. He didn't like this
army – "that fellow Dobson's not a gentleman!" he say, real
posh like.

So I reckon I toud you my bit. They all said arterwards I'd
done a marvellous thing taking old Duggy's Land-Rover and
taking the word to the boys like that. Bob here reckons that just
about saved the whul' world. And I must say thass lucky I did.
And do that damned Major, and Clifford Brown, hadn't bin so
rude to me I don't suppose I should ha' thought on it. Shows –
that pays to be polite – even to peasants – don't it?

Chapter Six

(From Jessie Hurlock's writings left in Sibford Maltings.)

Well I guess from my point of view I was just too busy to worry much about anything, those first few months.

You see I had this hang-up about the people milling about outside our little Shangri-La with nothing much to eat. I just couldn't relate to the idea. So I built up this big scene where all the folks who thought like me – and that included our doctor, he was a sweetie-pie, Dr Ahmed, a Pakistani – got together this committee and took over Sibford Maltings. We turned it into a refugee camp and we prevailed on the gallant territorials to be a bit selective.

They still turned most of the people back at the bridges and the various road blocks they'd set up but we got it so that all unaccompanied children were automatically taken in and so, at the boy's discretion, were women with no men especially if they had children with them. I remember my women's lib days and how all this would have seemed so sexist to me. But after the CRASH . . .

I was delighted when Bob's party got elected. He and I didn't always see eye-to-eye over the refugee question – he was all for letting the kids in – Bob was always knocked over by any kid – but the grown-ups he didn't want. I knew that nature abhors a vacuum and that we'd have to take some sooner or later. Better take 'em on our own terms in our own good time than have 'em all come in a rush. And I eventually think I persuaded Bob – I farm, they would strengthen our community. Send not to hear for whom the bell tolls; and they were as human as we were and had just as much right to live. My pressure groups said take 'em in. Make them work their passage for three years and then give 'em bits of land. Maybe it was my American pioneer ancestors that were talking to me. And there were all those empty acres to be filled – and cultivated – when the oil finally did run out. We were straight back in a sexist world again. My God – how sexist!

Anyways we took these refugees into the Maltings and did for 'em as best we could, and I travelled around on a wheel begging blankets, and worrying hell out of everybody to take the kids into their homes, and worrying hell out of the Council to fix it so the grown-ups could be farmed out to people who had bits of land, or to farmers. They passed a law that any outsider would have the right, if he worked three years for a native, to a bit of land himself.

I wasn't all that popular in those days. I suppose folks felt the outsiders as a threat – kind of infiltrating into our area. But I did my damnedest and I believe a lot of folks were secretly on my side. We got quite a scene going.

I suppose the two main schools of thought in the district were the folks who thought the oil would come back and those who knew it wouldn't. People like Clifford Brown just couldn't believe the world could be without oil. Clifford was always using the word "regularised". It was his favourite word. But you see we could see the North Sea from Cragpit and I couldn't help noticing that the tanker traffic just stopped. There were no more tankers from the north. Now I know you can't abandon things like deep-sea oil wells and platforms and all the rest of it for months on end and just expect them to go to work again. The whole thing had broken down. There would never be any oil. That was it. Bob knew this and that's why he went on training his oxen and wishing we had a stallion in the district.

Then when this fucking army came there was a whole new ball-game.

You see, the bad news was that in the eyes of a lot of people in

Then when this fucking army came there was a whole new ball-game.

You see, the bad news was that in the eyes of a lot of people in Gretford and district things looked a lot better. The army brought gas, or petrol as I guess I should call it. There was a lot of the stuff left in England I suppose. After all – twenty million cars suddenly disappeared off the roads and several million diesel lorries, and the government had no doubt stashed away a few million tons of it for emergencies. So in came the tanker trucks, with the army, and for most of the folks it looked like deliverance.

People were as soft as shit you see. The average Englishman before the CRASH couldn't lift a brick off the floor. And there they were – the old dowagers and retired gents and the folks who'd been on the dole for half their lives – or all of them – having to work. They got their bits of land all right, but they had to work them. For the first time in their lives what they were going to eat was related to the amount of honest toil they were prepared to put in. They hated it!

A lot of these cats stood by and watched London Farming's tractors ploughing out their hard-dug gardens – most of them by then planted up with seed – and heaved a sigh of relief! This is what they were used to – them – they – you left things to them in those days – "Nanny" as Bob used to call it – the government – the "Labour". You never had to worry about anything so long as you filled in the appropriate forms. Funny thing about forms – we used to be surrounded by them – the postman never called without putting a few through the letter-box. Now we've forgotten what they looked like. They really were a major part of our living. I remember this crazy guy back in about 1998 starting the Burn-a-Form-Society. "There's nothing that's legal about us that the government may want to know which we can't tell them in a letter," he said. "Burn all forms!" That's one thing about the English that slays me – you always get some crazy English guy who rears up and says to hell with "Nanny" when "Nanny" goes too far.

But the real good ol' Suffolk 'bors weren't so tickled at having their new gardens ploughed over. I shall never forget the enthusiasm that some folks – real country folks – the women as well as the men – accepted their new pieces of land when the Council handed them out. Before or since I've never seen men or women work like it! But they knew they were working for themselves you see. This was real "private enterprise" that the Conservatives were always blabbing about. And this Clifford Brown was like a crazy man. He came along with the army and made them pull down and burn – can you imagine it – burn the little barns and cowsheds and pig-sties that the people had put up, and used good fuel to bulldoze the fences, and so all that garden area was ploughed up. Why the little plants – broad beans and early peas and early potatoes – were already beginning to show through the ground. I stood by and wept! I felt this was the sickest thing I had ever seen in my life.

The people had carried leaf-mould and compost, slurry out of London Farming's huge slurry lagoon, seaweed, and anything else they could find to manure their little bits of land.

And in the event the land gave hardly any crop at all. Brown ploughed the land up and sowed barley over most of it – God knows what he thought our area was going to do with all that barley – live on beer I suppose – but it had been a barley farm before and that was all he could think about. He managed to get hold of some herbicide to put on it and he moved heaven and earth to get some nitrogen but he just couldn't get any. There were still stores of fertiliser in the country but the army just couldn't get round to getting it to Clifford.

In the event the barley was bad news. He hardly got a crop at all. Of course when you think of it – for sixty years that farm had not had an ounce of muck on it – it had been doused with bag nitrogen and poisons of all sorts and grown nothing but barley. That land was hooked. Bob and I knew it would take years before it could be got back into good heart again.

Meanwhile it was obvious that it would be Cragpit Farm that would feed the people next winter. Our land was in fine heart –

we had always been organic freaks – thank God there were quite
a lot of us about by *20 - - -* and our crops were as good as ever
and we grew a great variety. In my intervals from wheeling
around begging blankets I tended my seeds. I intended to spend
the next few years just multiplying them up so that future
generations should have plenty of variety. I even grew some
flowers. Bob said about the flowers I was like Nero playing the
violin while Rome burnt, but I told him to go to hell.

That bastard Brown left us alone for the whole of that summer.
But I knew he bore us a grudge that he wouldn't forget. It must
have galled him terribly to watch his own two thousand acres of
barley coming to nothing while our farm stood out like a fruitful
green oasis. Everybody noticed it. All the real country people
commented on it – constantly. They couldn't help but draw
conclusions could they?

The army were just a damned nuisance. I knew that it was right
that food should be transported from the country to the
townspeople – but it didn't need an army to do it. Little groups
of so-called soldiers were stuck on everybody's farm, and they
had to be fed, and they were the most worthless set of men I ever
saw.

We were lucky – we had Hugh Giles billeted on us. He had
two guys with him – one was his batman as he called him –
Marshall. "Marshall!" he used to shout. "Where is the bastard!"

My was it a comfort to us having Hughie and not some other
geezer! The soldiers were supposed to snoop for hidden food you
see, or oil, or anything like that. And on our farm there was
plenty to snoop for. We'd always been a real self-sufficient farm
you see. We'd never gone in for monoculture. You name it we
grew it or raised it. And we had the diesel Mick Miller had
brought us in the *Suffolkman*. We paid him for that with produce:
enough bacon, ham and wheat flour and tatties to last him a
couple of months.

But Hughie didn't care a dam' what we had stashed away. He
helped us eat it though. And his contribution was endless bottles
of Scotch.

I remember the day he joined us. It was all a bit of a wangle him coming to us, and I heard privately that that snake Brown tried to get him moved when he heard about it and some other bastard sent to us. Funny thing – Dobson was as weak as hell and let himself be ruled by Brown in everything but Hugh was a regular and a guards officer and had quite a pull up above somewhere and he did more or less what he wanted.

"Do you know," he said the first evening he came to us, over a bottle of whisky of course, "I've known you, Bob, for forty years! You're an awful bastard but, funny thing Jessie, I'm fond of the old devil in my funny old way! He hasn't changed much has he? Being married to a beautiful young gel, that's what does it."

We tried to pump him about the military government but he was a terrible man to get anything out of. He talked for effect – not to convey information. His mind moved in some peculiar way.

"Army?" he said. "It's no bloody army. Thank God we've got a navy if that's the army. If we have got a navy. My God, they wouldn't have allowed these chaps in the mess in my day. Except as waiters and they wouldn't have been any good at that. Look at Dobson. Well really Bob – the man's not a gentleman is he? Shouldn't wear the King's uniform. Wouldn't have allowed the chap in our mess. Top up, Bob".

He tried to persuade Bob to join the army though. "Best thing you could do. Farming's finished. Join this mob – I can't stand their guts but it's the only thing you can do. I had a big shoot up in Lincolnshire you know, Bob – that's why I haven't been down this way for some years. And the blasted poachers came and stripped it bare. Not a feather left. They netted the fields and even poisoned the damned fish pond! Cads! there's no other word for them. I don't mind the odd didikoi nicking a pheasant or two – good luck to him. But they wiped the lot. And out of season. I'd shoot the bloody lot of 'em."

"Where did you join this mob, Hugh?" asked Bob.

"Well I was on half pay you see, Bob. Left the Guards. But

I happened to be at Camberley when all this nonsense started and I was a good friend of Johnnie Nightingale. I was on the reserve of course, and so I joined his lot. He put me on the strength. As you know the Guards were in Germany. No good sending me there. Johnnie Nightbird's all right – a bit of a sober bastard but he's a good soldier. You sign on with us, Bob. It's the best you can do. Farming's finished, that's for sure. No future in farming."

"I shouldn't have thought there was a future in anything else," I murmured and Bob said: "What do you do in this Fred Karno's army?" I was always hearing about Fred Karno's army; it was one of the many tedious jokes you British have. Fred Karno was some old British comedian or other.

"Oh we get around!" said Hughie. "I told Marshall the other day – don't loot any more gin. Haven't got room for it in the trucks. Stick to whisky. I will say this, Bob – they may be awful cads, some of them; but I haven't wanted for anything since I joined 'em. Everything of the best. Don't allow raping in my company though. Some of the other units are bastards. Looting yes – but girls – they have to be willing. And when they're big enough they're old enough."

"Well what's this government we hear about, Hugh?"

"Government? There's no damned government. King ought to take over again but he's buggered off. Don't blame him. Couldn't stay at Windsor with all dead bodies around. Wha!"

"Well what is the government?"

"There isn't any damned government. What do you need a government for anyway? There's just this Service Corps chap Wicklow. Says he's Commander-in-Chief. Imagine – the British Army commanded by a Service Corps wallah! God bless my soul. Go on, Bob – top up. Marshall's got plenty in the truck. Drunken bastard though – and yet he's a good chap. God bless him. Do you know – he was in my regiment before we both took the bowler hat? Just luck we met up in this lot."

We tried to keep him to the point but he was hopeless. "Does this man Wicklow's command stretch to London?" I asked.

"London? There isn't any damned London. Do you know, Jessie, I often think of the old times. Do you remember London in the old days? Imagine a Rolls drawing up outside the old Ritz, before the Arabs bought it, and the chauffeur opening the door and a beautiful woman stepping out – one of those wonderful sparkling dresses they used to wear? It's all gone now my dear. Did you ever go to Chez Victo when they opened it? We're going to miss it you know."

We couldn't get any more out of him.

I tried to pump Dobson. He was a stupid kind of guy. Didn't really know his arse from his elbow, as Hughie so succinctly put it. I met Clifford Brown in *The Crown* one day. He hadn't gone there to drink – the man was a teetotaller – but to arse-creep to the military.

"Why did you put the boot into all those gardens the people had?" I said.

"Gardens?" he said in his thin precise voice. "People scratching about like peasants? It was London Farming land anyway."

"London Farming? There isn't any London Farming. There isn't any damned London. Just forget it."

"Well there is as far as I'm concerned Mrs Hurlock."

"You got plenty of oil?"

"There are large stocks in the country. The army have the oil situation well in hand. There are still large reserves under the North Sea. The whole thing will be regularised again."

"Regularised my foot!"

He looked at his watch. "Well I'm afraid I must be going, Mrs Hurlock," he said. "I have an appointment with the adjutant."

I know I shouldn't have said it. But I could never hold my tongue when I ought to do. "Adjutant my arse!" I said.

I never told Bob of this conversation but I've kicked myself many times since.

Chapter Seven

by Bob Hurlock

After harvest things came to a head pretty quickly. London Farming's wheat and barley gave abysmal yields, as everyone who knew anything about farming knew they would. All that the land seemed to be able to grow, without the usual massive supplies of NPK[1] that used to be put on it, was very little but sterile brome and couch grass. Farming in England – or agribusiness as it had become called – was just about ready to crash anyway even before the CRASH. Many of us had seen it coming. Half a century of burning all straw, before that was made illegal in 1994. No muck, massive applications of fertiliser, and lashings of poisons; fungicides, insecticides, bactericides, virucides and, worst of all, herbicides had simply taken all heart out of the land. Certain weeds, such as wild oats, black grass and sterile brome had got worse and worse because no herbicide seemed to be able to poison them completely without poisoning the crop too. London Farming's two hundred and fifty cows were like a good deed in a naughty world: most of East Anglia had no animals on it at all, except us two-legged ones. The animals had been divorced from the soil and their dung was missing. Agribusiness had broken the essential natural cycle: soil – plant – animal – soil. All human sewerage, of course, was pumped out to sea, so there was that constant drain on our fertility. And

---

[1] Nitrogen, Phosphorous and Potash.

monoculture, the growing of one crop only, year after year, made necessary by the huge cost of farm machinery, had taken its toll also and had encouraged a build-up of various pests and diseases which required more and more poisonous chemicals to combat.

And then when the CRASH came there was a sudden cutting-off of all fertilisers and pesticides. The result was disastrous.

Whom the gods wish to destroy they first make mad. Clifford Brown cast beady eyes on the fine crops at Cragpit Farm. We hadn't used any artificial fertiliser for thirty years because for that time my father and I had been organic farmers. We fed our soil with good muck, rotated our crops, and our land was in fine fettle.

Brown came to see me just before our corn harvest. He was accompanied by a so-called "officer" with a pistol in a holster. A little show of force I thought.

He stood in my yard looking over the gate at the finest crop of wheat you ever saw.

"I – er – feel I should congratulate you on your wheat crop," he said.

"I feel you should too," I answered. "There's a couple of tons to the acre there. What yields do you think you're going to get?"

"Oh – er it'll be better next year after the supply of nitrogen has been regularised."

"Well if it is you can have my share," I said. "I don't use the nasty stuff."

"Hurlock," he said. "I'm in charge of agriculture and food as you know. I think I'll take your corn into our silos at London Farming. We can see that it's properly dried and keep an eye on it there."

"We are quite capable of looking after our own grain, Clifford," I said.

"Well you may be, but I think I'll send for it all the same. You'll get your fair share back again as you need it of course. You'll get your ration cards the same as everybody else."

"You can stuff your rations cards up your arse, Clifford old boy," I said. "And you can leave my wheat where it is. You're so keen on preserving the pre-CRASH pattern of ownership. Well I own this land like you don't, and never did, own London Farming land. You're only a manager. And you've grown practically nothing on the land you farm this year. Who the hell are you to come and tell me what to do with my own crops? This is my farm and I'll farm it; and these are my crops and I'll look after 'em. I'm perfectly willing to give my fair share of them to go to England to feed hungry people, and to feed the people of Gretford come to that, but I've got animals here – and a lot of 'em – and I intend to keep back enough grain and spuds and roots to feed 'em."

"It's no good going on Hurlock – I'm afraid I'm the boss and I've got the army behind me. I can confiscate this land if I want to. If I don't like the way it's being farmed, all I have to do is take it in hand. We've got surplus tractor capacity now at London Farming – it might well be better to take this land in hand."

By now my temper was such that I was having difficulty in controlling it. "You may have this so-called army behind you but I've got the people of this district behind me. Do you remember how they voted in the election? And if you thieve my land, everyone will know that their property will come next. You'll have every man and woman in the country against you. You just mind your business and I'll mind mine. And you might as well go and mind it now – I've got work to do!"

"This is my business, Hurlock," he said. And he and his hit-man got in their staff car and drove away.

After this I felt a great unease, but there was nothing to do but go on quietly with my arrangements for the harvest. Then one day Jean came running into the workshop where I was working on our Italian reaper-and-binder (I had imported one of these years before from Italy and it was the apple of my eye – an Olympia, and nothing like it). "Daddy!" she called. "There are three huge combines cutting our oats!"

I walked as fast as I could to the big ten-acre oatfield. What she said was right. The oats were not anything like ready to cut. In any case my habit was to cut them with a binder, "church them three times" as the old saying was (that is leave them in a stook to dry out for three Sundays) then feed them in the sheaf to the cattle. These ate the straw as well as the grain, and all and this method of feeding explained why I always had the best looking cattle in the country. And those oats were not ready to cut!

Standing by the gate was a corporal and four soldiers: all armed. I went up to them.

"Don't know nothing about it, guvnor," says this shifty-looking corporal. "My orders are to prevent any interference with the harvesters, that's all."

"But those oats aren't fit to cut!"

"I wouldn't know whether they was oats or daffodils, old boy. All the same to me. I'm only obeying orders."

I strode over and stood in the way of the approaching combines. I hate combines. A lazy-man's way of harvesting. The grain is not allowed to dry naturally in the sheaf in the field, and later to cure in the rick; but is bashed out long before it's ready to be threshed and then it has to be artificially dried, with copious use of fuel oil; and the whole thing is wrong.

The three combines advanced towards me. Over my own field – raping my own good oats! I stood my ground. I held up my hands to sign to the driver of the first combine to stop. He just kept coming on. I had to jump for my life. It was unbelievable! They were not local men driving – London Farming's old employees – they were soldiers. I knew no local man could have been got to do it.

I dashed back to the farm and saddled my horse. I rode hell-for-leather to *The Crown Hotel*. There I found Dobson. "What the hell's those bastards doing in my oatfield?" I shouted at him.

He pretended that he didn't know what was happening. Maybe he didn't – he was a big enough fool.

"I leave all that sort of thing to Mr Brown," he said. "After all – he's got a BSc. Agric."

"BSc. Agric!" I shouted. "Well you can tell him to stuff it up his arse! And order him to get his filthy combines out of my oatfield or I'll have every man, woman and child in this district turn against him, and you, and the whole bloody boiling of you!"

I stormed over to Brown's office. "Take your bloody, shitting machines out of my unripe oats!" I shouted. "Only a jumped-up fool like you wouldn't see the damned oats aren't ripe! What the hell do you know about farming – you and your BSc. Agric? You can't grow a bloody thing yourself without half a ton of NPK per acre – or hectare as you call it – and the bloody sprays going up and down non-stop the whole year. You're bloody useless. Take your damned machines out of my crop and piss off out of it!"

At least as far as I can remember that was the tenor of my remarks. I suppose, as things were, I was less than tactful. This stupid little man leapt to his feet. "Hurlock!" he shouted. "Get out of my office! And if you try to interfere with any of my men I will have you shot!"

And I'm blowed if he didn't call an armed guard, who had obviously been hanging about in the next room in anticipation of my visit.

I had to ride back to my farm and, day after day, I had to see those horrible machines crawling over my good land. I desperately hated seeing heavy machinery like that on land anyway: the compaction caused by heavy machinery on England's land was one of the contributory causes of its breakdown of structure.

The first evening at home was one long indignation meeting. The children were all for asking Dike, who happened to drop in that evening, to go and gather up his old territorial platoon and dig up their weapons and take on Dobson, and his army, and all the rest of it.

"What right have a lot of silly men from the Midlands got to come here anyway?" said Robin, who had just had his eleventh birthday. "I've got my two-two. I wouldn't mind going and shooting a few!"

"They might shoot you first 'bor!" said Dike. "No, no. We can't take that ru'd. Softly, softly, catchee monkey."

"What do you think Dike?" I asked. "How do you think the

local people will take this lot?"

"Well us real country boys will back you up to the hilt, Bob. You can depend on that. But we can't fight a bloody army. They say they've got two hundred men at Willingham Castle."

"We should go to the law!" said Susan.

"They are the bloody law," said Dike.

"That horrible little man Brown said that he has a mind to take away our farm, Dike."

"Do he do he'll be gooin' a bit too far I reckon Maaster," said Dike, in his lovely broad Suffolk accent. When I heard that sort of talk I felt comforted. Surely there was strength and resilience here and the capacity to survive? Dike and his forebears had lived in this country ever since they came over in the long ships from the other side of the Viking Ocean. They wouldn't give up easily now.

"I wonder if the people would stand up and fight," I said. I had doubts about it. "You see – the English are a terribly law-abiding people. Nanny had ruled their every action so long that they've had all the independence taken out of them. These army people have uniforms on. Then – they have oil. They can bring the people oil. Do you know – nothing has made the people unhappier – feel more insecure – than the petrol running out. The true country people would love smallholdings you know, Dike. You would, I know. But the others – nine-tenths of 'em used to drive into Randersfield or Ipswich every day and work as clerks. They'd never done a day's work in their lives. As soon as they bent over those spades their backs began to creak. I think they were quite glad to see the old tractors crawling over that lands again."

"Well what the hell's a' gooin' to happen when the oil do run out?" said Dike.

"Your guess is as good as ours Dike, old boy," said Jessie.

After Dike had left, and the children had gone to bed, Jessie and I sat up for a long time over a little fire we lit, just to cheer ourselves up. We sat in silence for a long while. Jessie came and sat on the arm of my chair and put her hand on my shoulder.

"Don't worry, old Bear!" she said. "This is only one harvest. Things will work out. I know they will!"

"Those bloody machines!" I groaned. "Those machines!"

"I know, Bear!"

I tried to stop myself. I tried like hell. I am not philosophical enough, I suppose. Not in proper control of myself. I am ashamed to say I put my face down in my hands and wept.

Chapter Eight

by Dike Randle

(Recorded by Eliza Keeble)

I was some angry about poor ol' Bob's corn. That fair riled me. "Thaas a dam' shame!" I say to the other blokes in *The Barge* next night. And they all agreed with me. They was whully riled.

And that harvest worn't the last of it. There was more to come. I'd taken to gooin' to Bob's every day to do a job here and there – like nearly all the rest of us I was unemployed you see. The men were idle and the tractors done the work. Made no sense to me, nor yet to nobody else.

And one day along comes this sergeant and ten men waving a piece of paper and saying as he'd got to make off with Bob's pigs!

London Farming had lost all their pigs you see. We all knew they would. You see pigs in them Belsen housen, as they used to be called, could only be kept alive by constant jabs and injections and medications and God knows what all. First they got swine vesicular disease which killed all the piglets and pulled down the sows and then along came swine fever and that was that. The whul' lot turned their toes up – do they didn't they were knocked on the head to git 'em out the way. The corpses were all sent away in the army lorries – to be fed to people what didn't know better I suppose.

So that made that bugger Brown want to stock up again with ol'
Bob's pigs. Now a better bunch of gilts and sows you never did
see. Ol' Bob loved 'em. They was a picture. Six Welsh sows
he had and half a dozen saddlebacks, and a gret ol' Welsh boar.
He kept 'em out o'doors, behind the electric fence; and he moved
'em about over the land so they never got the worms; moved 'em
on to clean ground too, often – and they was a treat. That did
you good to see 'em!

Then along came this dam' silly sergeant a'waving this bit of
paper and saying they was to be requisitioned. They was to goo
to London Farming.

I was whully stammed at how calm Bob took it. "All right," he
say. "Come you into the kitchen," he say. "Bring these gallant
soldiers in too. And Jessie may find you up a glass of home-
brewed beer. I'll goo and git the sows – have to git 'em into the
shed for you to load."

I couldn't rightly believe it. Ol' Bob was easily riled you know.
I've known the oud boy for most of his life and I'd say it before
him – he's not the best of tempered man do he's put out. No, no.
That 'on't do.

So off he goo upstairs. I didn't think naathin' about it – didn't
know where he'd gone.

We sit in the kitchen and shares round this brew and then – the
others didn't hear it but I did. Thirteen shots. I knew what it was
– Robin's two-two rifle.

Goo to hell I thought. Thass put the cat among the pigeons.
I knew dam' well what he'd a'done.

Sure enough – in he comes as cool as a cucumber. He'd hid the
rifle I make no doubt.

"I've got the pigs ready for you," he say. "Robin – show the
soldiers to Star Piece – where the piggies are."

I couldn't help it – I goo with 'em.

And there they were, all round the troughs. Ol' Bob had
chucked 'em their last meal. And they was pork – the whul' lot
on 'em! Dead as mutton.

Blast there was hell to pay!

This here sergeant, he rants and he roars. Bob just stood laughing at him! He put his hands on his old sides and laugh and laughs – I thought he'd kill hisself!

"Take the sows back to master Brown," he say. "He 'on't need the boar – he can fuck 'em hisself!"

Well blast they arrests poor ol' Bob. They takes him off. They locks him up. There's to be a court-martial. And meanwhile this Bugger Brown sends a big squad o' men to sarch the farmstead!

Ol' Giles warn't there then – they'd sent him away to the Sheers somewhere. Do he'd a'helped ol' Bob I make no doubt. They seemed a bit scared o' ol' Giles – he was more of a gent like – a real soldier.

So they pushes past poor Jessie and sarches the whul' place and they finds I don' know what-all. There was whisky stashed away – what Giles had left – there was grub of all sorts – and worst of all there was this here diesel. What ol' Mick Miller had a'brought in his barge.

I remember standing by poor Jessie when they found this diesel. She'd bin a'crying poor little dear. I was trying for to comfort her. But when they finds this diesel, she just stood there and laughed. "The shit's in the electric fan now, Dike boy!" she says. And I has to laugh with her. Right through she was as plucky as hell – do she did cry it were for rage not for weakness.

Well they was like bloody vandals. They takes the lot away, they drags Jessie and the little ol' kiddies out and carts 'em away to Sibford Maltings – where the refugees were put.

As for Bob – I doubt he'll tell you about what happen to him but he was sent off to Cambridgeshire somewhere to be put in a prison camp and cut down trees.

Old Brown had his revenge all right. I hoop he enjoyed it. Do that didn't pay the miserable sod.

Well all the real ol' country boys they was furious! They all liked Bob you see – and they loved his little American lady. And the kids were popular. Everybody liked that family – I never heard a word agin 'em.

People were furious.

But that fared to be the end of it – the whul family fared to be wiped out. Of course we looked arter 'em like. They didn't want for what we could find up for 'em do they were in Sibford Maltings.

Now as time wore on there was more and more discontent. Everyone was unemployed you see. There was only a handful of chaps employed by London Farming and they took overnight all the land. They took in Bob's farm o' course. It was the only land that had a mite of heart in it. The rest of it'd bin farmed from the bag too long. And there warn't no more bags.

So everybody had to troop along to London Farming's office like a lot o' damned beggars, every Friday, and stand in a queue and git their dole cards. Not the gentry mind – Brown'd send them theirs – creeping bastard do he was. Then they'd line up at ol' Alum the grocers to git little doles of food. If it hadn't bin for Bob and Jessie's farm we'd all ha' starved to dead I reckon that year. But they'd growed everything. Every mortal crop you could think of. That fed the district and we all knew it did too. Brown couldn't hide that fact.

Then I'm damned if Brown didn't snatch up all the bullocks that Bob had a'bin breaking to the yoke and killed 'em all and shipped 'em off to the Sheers for meat! You wouldn't ha' thought it possible! That a man could be such a dam' fule! That fare made me want to puke! And nobody else liked it either – nobody what'd got na sense. That didn't bear thinking about.

Dobson was a damned fule too. He riled the nonconformists by the way he carried on. There was plenty of teenyboppers see, what had been used to the American airmen. The airmen had all gone to hell knows where but the girls hadn't. Dobson used to have 'em into his bedroom by the half dozen! Proper orgies they had in *The Crown Hotel*. That didn't make na difference to me what they did but that whully riled some of the folk. And of course they was all on the hops (beer) – the whul' dam' lot of 'em. The only sensible thing Dobson did was to make Brown start a'malting of barley. Brown didn't know a mite about it o' course – he didn't know anything that was any dam' use. But there were those that did and they got a maltin's a'gooin' and a brewery and the army spent half its time pissed. That was thumbs a'wash every night – thumbs a'wash as they carried their piss-pots to empty 'em out of the window.

They was a rum lot! Soldiers! They was no more soldiers than my auntie's budgerigar. We didn't mind 'em getting drunk, but it was what they did when they was drunk! There was rape and pillage. No woman was safe. Nor little ol' maathers neither. (Eliza's note: maather means young girl in Suffolk.) They were after the lot.

And o' course the men began to get riled! Some men joined the army – I suppose they thought if you couldn't beat 'em, join 'em. But they was sent right away – to the Sheers somewhere – and they never come back. And I don't think that'd pay 'em do they did come back. I think some of 'em might git an ash plant down their hids.

Well, that got worse and worse. We had to see nigh on all the harvest taken off to the Sheers in trucks. Whatever else, they had oil to spare on, this here army had plenty for that purpose. Off it all went. Left us just enough to goo half-hungry on. And the poor little orphans – there were lots on 'em you see – Jessie's lot had seen to that – they'd let 'em in. They was billeted out – nigh everybody had a few of 'em. There wasn't enough grub to goo round 'em all.

We had this meeting. We all got so fed up that we circulated it about and called a meeting in Gretford Church. People came from miles around. The church was full. There wasn't many troops in Gretford just then – most on 'em were back at Willingham I don't doubt – and ol' Dobson was all of a laather. He was a stupid little man and he wasn't fit to be in charge of a sweet shop.

And we all goes at it hammer an' tongs – what we was a'gooin' to do about it and how we was gooin' to say this an that and complain to the High Command an' I don't know what-all – and then in comes the soldiers! Two platoons of 'em.

"Everybody out!" shouts this Captain what come with 'em.

Brute of a man he were – as well he had his Sam Browne on do you'd ha' took him for an ape!

We knew where we was then. There waren't no more doubt about it. We knew where we was and how we stood togither. We knew that one day that'd got to be sorted out. That take a long time to rile a Suffolkman but we was some riled then, I can tell you.

Chapter Nine

by Bob Hurlock

Although the court-martial was farcical, it was a terrible experience for me.

I had never before been on the wrong side of the law. I had never thought that such a thing could happen to me. I had been fined, in my time, for a trivial motoring offence, and during my army career had once or twice been reprimanded by commanding officers for minor matters, but in other courts-martial of my experience I had always been one of the "goodies" as it were: trying somebody else. It had never occurred to me that I would ever get into any serious trouble with the law about anything. That sort of thing happened to other people. I was taken, in the back of a truck (if one is "officer-type" one is used to being carried in the front of trucks) to Willingham castle. I was escorted by a corporal and two men. This annoyed me – I had been, after all, a captain in the army and should have been escorted by an officer of equal rank. I was locked up in a room at the castle, and kept there for three days. I was not allowed to get word to Jessie.

I asked if I could have Hugh Giles as Prisoner's Friend, but was told that he refused to appear for me. I was terribly hurt at this. After all, we had been old friends. I learned afterwards he wasn't even aware at what had happened. But after a lifetime of having been treated with respect, it hurt me terribly to be ordered about and shut up like any common criminal. I had never felt

more thoroughly unhappy and insecure. And I worried miserably
about Jessie and the children, and what was left of my farm. I sat
in my cell feeling consumed with bitterness. The court-martial, as
I have said, was a farce. I was allowed to call no witnesses for
the defence. My Prisoner's Friend was an enemy. I was
sentenced to a year's imprisonment with hard labour. Along with
five other people I was put in the back of a truck, handcuffed,
and sent right across Suffolk to a large military camp at
Wretham, in the Brecklands. When we arrived we were solemnly
warned by the camp commandant that – if we escaped – our
wives and families would be shot.

I was put into a hut with forty other men. We were not ill-
treated, or knocked about. Every morning we were marched out
into the pine forest (the Brecklands resembles our own part of
Suffolk in largely being planted up by the Forestry Commission)
and there we cut trees. We clear-felled, which seemed a terrible
waste of trees; they were only half grown and should merely
have been thinned so that the trees left could have grown on to
maturity. But the purpose of the exercise was to provide fuel.

The coal mines had all, apparently, ceased production. The
ones that had escaped destruction had mostly flooded when they
were left by their miners. There had been such a breakdown in
organisation, such panic, such running hither and thither, that
mines, railways, all large undertakings simply collapsed. And it
was now late autumn, and very cold. The powers that had seized
the land wanted fuel for their fires, and trees seemed the easiest
answer. And so there we were, the bolshie or the wicked,
marched out into the pine forests every morning to cut trees.

It was not a hard job. We were each given a quota to cut for
the day, and when we had cut it we could knock off. We used
axes – they'd buggered up all the chain saws. If we failed to cut
the quota in the day we had no supper that night, nor breakfast
the next morning. I could have cut mine with one hand tied
behind my back. The majority of the prisoners, I supposed,
worked so badly, or with such ill-grace, that the quota had to be
set low.

The man sleeping in the next bunk to me was an engineer from the Black Fens.

"How did you get here?" I asked him, the first evening I turned in. It was pretty cold in the hut, but they were not mean with blankets. We sat on the edges of our bunks with blankets over our shoulders.

"Trying to save my country," he said.

"Did you lead a revolt?"

"Not really. You see – our Fens depended on diesel oil. I don't think people realised that so much before. Once we had windmills, and the wind was free. But the land was sinking all the time – and we soon needed steam to pump the water out up into the rivers. Then came diesel engines – and then electric power. Now after the CRASH the electric power cut off and that was that. I was the engineer responsible for the Lydney area. We had plenty of diesel pumps though – and we could have gone on working with these, and at least kept some of our fens dry. But the diesel ran out of course. As you know the government had been stock-piling it at Peterborough. We began to make use of that. Then this bloody Fred Karno's army stepped in and said they were the government and the fuel was under their control. They continued to let us have some – but not enough. Fen after fen was flooded – fens that could have been kept pumped out. We were madly trying to devise other means; getting hold of old steam engines – some people were even trying to knock up wind pumps again. Out of steel you know. But we needed time. The army said they needed the fuel for more important purposes – and that at any rate there was no immediate food shortage – we could let the fens flood – and pump them dry later when the oil came from America. Imagine! Did you ever hear such arrant nonsense? The pump-houses are all flooded now of course – those pumps will never work again. Well, the old Fenman – the Fen Tiger – came out in them again, I suppose, when they saw the water creeping up in the fields, coming over their doorsteps very often – flooding their good black earth. Well they poured into Lydney at first and demanded something of us. I could do nothing. Then they said; "March on Peterborough and take the oil!" We did. I went with them of course – we took a few lorries we still had diesel for – and a couple of thousand marched. We were met by the army – they told us to disperse – we wouldn't – they fired shots – we rushed them – most of the chaps had shotguns, or at least sticks – there was a battle and several hundred Fenmen were killed and God knows how many wounded. We overran one lot of soldiers; more came – mortars – armoured cars – tanks – the lot. There was one hell of a battle. A hell of a lot more chaps were killed – I got this . . . (he showed me a leg wound, completely healed now) and the rest were taken prisoner. And here we are. Most of the chaps in this hut are Fenmen. And let me tell you brother – our turn is coming one day."

"What do you intend to do?"

"Don't you worry. Our turn will come. But the Fens are finished. The whole of the Great Level must be flooded by now – a quarter of the food production of England gone. And I don't suppose it will ever be salvaged."

I asked him if he thought help would come from outside the country. "No," he said. "Look – the Yanks would have been here to help the Old Country if they could have. They're in a worse mess than us. You know – you hear a lot in this camp. People from all over, here."

"What about Europe?"

"They can't bring us oil. They've nothing to offer us – or to want from us."

"The Old Commonwealth?"

"Where's the shipping to come from? It takes great organisations to keep the big ships going – fuel them – victual them – maintain them. And what do they want from us? No. We're alone."

"What the devil are we to do?"

"Do? Fight. Somehow we must fight – but I'm damned if I know how."

There was a young chap in the hut – what I would have called an intellectual. He was there because he had refused some silly order of the Army. He was a countryman, although intellectual, and he had theories as to what had happened to us.

"You look," he said to me. "We're all countrymen in here – in this camp. And our guards are all townsmen. At least the new ones – some of the old sweats were simply in the Army and now have to do what they are told. But the bigger part of the army is of city lay-abouts taken on since the CRASH. And do you know why it's like that? They're scared stiff of us – but they know they can't do without us. When the oil runs out – and it will – someone's got to get to work with a hoe and a spade. They know they can't, they'll have to. So their only hope is to gather in this army and rule us country people by force – and make us work like serfs to grow their food for them. That's what it's got down to. They'll form a feudal system – you see – they'll parcel the land out among themselves and rule the rest of us by force and lord it like feudal barons."

"What do you intend to do" I said.

"Me – I'm waiting until the oil runs out. Then we'll all starve. But if we do survive – at least I think we'll see the downfall of this regime."

As for me, I had one thought in my head, and that was to escape. I would risk them shooting my family. I never believed it could be anything but a threat: a bluff. They were ordinary Englishmen after all; they would never shoot women and children. It was just that mad captain at Willingham.

And about two months after I had arrived in the camp – the door of the hut opened and in walked Eli Woolpit and Dike Randle! They were shown in by their escort, went to two empty bunks that were there, and sat down unhappily enough.

I went over to them. "Don't say too much," I said. "Just sit quiet." I did not want too many people to see that we were old buddies, and perhaps likely to conspire together. I was afraid that, if such knowledge came to the guards, they might separate us.

Later, when their novelty had worn off, I started to talk to them. "How did you get in?" I asked.

Dike said: "Eli and I decided to kill that bugger Brown. We reckoned he'd better go first – then that bugger Dobson. Well we got caught. We bust into Brown's house – and some damned alarm went off, and the soldiers come and caught us. We hadn't got guns, see. We meant to do him in with an ash plant. Well – we didn't say what we were there for – said we wanted to rob him only. So they sent us here."

"Any news of Jessie?"

"She stay on in the house with the kids for a week. Then the army take over the house and all. They shoved some officer there – or he say he's an officer – I don't know what the hell he is. They shoved your missus and the kids in Sibford Maltings. They get fed all right there – you don't need to worry."

"One thing though," said Eli. "They tell me if I try to escape or cause any trouble, they'll shoot my missus. That's what they tell me."

"They do eh?" I said. "They told me the same – but it's bluff, that's all it is. To keep us quiet." I continued to make, secretly, my plans for escape. Life as it was going on for me was impossible. I did not mind the camp routine too much, as it happened; the work was easy, the food was rough but I had eaten rougher. I liked hearing from the other prisoners. It was interesting to get an idea of the state of the rest of the country. We had been isolated in Gretford District, since the CRASH. But it was too humiliating to be a prisoner in my own country, and to know that my wife and children were being humiliated too! I would rather have them all dead, in the final resort, and myself too, than to lie down to this humiliation much longer.

I thought of speaking to Dike and Eli about my plans for escape, and ask them if they wanted to take the risk of coming with me. I said nothing and the months went by.

We were working together in the forest one day, cutting trees. Dike, Eli, the engineer (whose name was Michael Self) and the intellectual (whose name was Tony Larkin) and I used to work together as much as we could. Provided we cut our quota of trees nobody minded what we did. It was thought that nobody would try to escape; the complete lack of food available in that part of the country would soon have laid him low, or at least that was the theory of our guards. In any case, guards were posted in all the rides around any block of forest that we were working in, and several more patrolled about among us with automatics.

It was a bitterly cold day, in April, with a biting east wind and sharp frost.

A military police corporal came up to our group and said: "I want six volunteers - you, you, you, you, you and you." We were all included.

"What have we got to do?" asked Michael.

"Never you mind - come with me."

He led us away, down a ride, to where a group of men, dressed as army officers, and a few civilians were standing with shotguns. One civilian, an East Anglian and obviously a game-keeper, came over to us and said: "We want you to do some brushing - for the guns." He was a Norfolk man, and brushing was his way of saying "beating". Driving the pheasants over the heads of the officers and "gentlemen".

"Go to hell," said Dike. "I never thought I'd ha' to brush pheasants for a bunch of ignorant bastards like that. In April too!"

We lined up in a ride, the guns moved off, the keeper stayed in the middle of our line and marshalled us. Then off we went - line abreast - beating the trees with sticks and shouting to scare the birds. To the six of us prisoners there was a corporal and two military policemen, all armed with machine carbines.

We made several drives. I must say the guns were deplorable. I never saw worse shooting in my life. Things became pretty confused, as they are inclined to do in pheasant drives in thick forest. A drive came in which we were very spread out - Eli, Dike and I were together a long way from the others and the military policeman who should have made our end of the line had got lost. We could hear the rest of the line beating and shouting well over to our left.

Suddenly, without any warning, Eli and I came out into a clearing in which stood a man dressed as a captain. He had a shotgun, and several birds at his feet. Eli, by the way, was "brushing" with an old broken axe-helve that he had picked up somewhere; I just had a stick.

As we came into view the captain said to Eli: "Pick that bird up there!"

Now Eli had been getting more morose and nasty-tempered as the days had gone by in the camp. He was not the type to submit to being messed about. He said: "Are you talking to me?"

"Of course I'm talking to you, fool!" said the man. "Do what you're told and don't answer back!"

Eli picked up the bird and went on walking towards him. I suddenly noticed the expression on the captain's face alter – and he stepped back and started to raise his gun – but too late – for him. Eli dashed at him and raised his axe-helve and brought it down on the man' head. I could hear his skull crack from where I was.

I ran up to them. "Eli!" I said. "We've got to get out of here – and damned quick!"

"I'll have no fucker talk to me like that!" said Eli.

"I don't blame you," I said. I picked up the man's shotgun. I saw that the gun was loaded. And just at that moment the military policeman who had got lost came out into the clearing. He got two charges of number-six shot through his chest before he could cough.

Eli stepped over and picked up the dead policeman's machine carbine. "Can you work that?" I said.

"Don't know as I can."

"Swap," I said, and we did. I made Eli take the dead captain's cartridge belt and I relieved the shot policeman of his two spare magazines.

Eli and I walked quickly into the trees.

"We can't leave Dike," I said, and we paused for a moment.

"We got to."

Just then I heard Dike's voice – coming from behind us in the clearing we had just left. "Goo to hell what's this?" I heard him exclaim.

Eli and I both ran back – and saw Dike and the military police sergeant standing looking at the two dead men. Eli shot the sergeant in the head. The shot didn't kill him so I finished him with a single shot from the automatic. There was plenty of shooting going on in that wood. Nobody would notice our shots.

"Take his gun!" I said to Dike. Dike did so, and also his spare magazine.

"Now follow me," I said.

And I began to run like hell through the trees. I ran in the direction away from the shooting – and away from where I knew our working party would be.

Dike and Eli followed me in single file. We had no breath for talking. We alternately walked and ran. We kept this up as long as we had breath – and we were fit men.

I had hoped that the pursuit might be delayed – even for quite a long time.

The dead men were not in a ride – but in a clearing, and it was quite likely that they would not be immediately discovered. It would be thought that the sergeant, the other policeman, and the two prisoners had simply got lost, and were wandering around, and would turn up in due course. In fact we could hear behind us the shots of another complete drive as we ran – the shooting went on for half an hour or so in a desultory way, and I was pretty sure that they had not started after us so long as I could hear the shooting.

The Brecklands is enormous; one of the biggest forests in England. I headed south-south west – into the heart of it. The sun was beginning to go down – it would soon be dusk.

Dike and Eli began to show distress at the pace. "You keep going you buggers!" I told them.

"I don't want to run meself to dead!" panted Dike. "Might as well get shot and have done with it."

We paused for a few minutes – and listened. We could hear nothing, but the cackle of an occasional pheasant going to roost, the wings of some mallard flying overhead, and the frozen wind in the trees.

We went on again, more slowly. We walked mostly down between rows of trees, where the going was very good. We came to a road – crossed it – went into the forest beyond. It got very dark underneath the pines. The sun was setting, behind clouds, and it is dark in those forests at midday even.

I led them on until it got quite dark. Then we stopped, and threw ourselves down on the pine needles.

After we had breathed hard for a bit I said: "Now. We'd better decide what to do next."

"You tell us," said Eli. "You're the captain."

"Right," I said. "I know Suffolk pretty well as a matter of fact. And what we will do is this. We will have a breather for half an hour – then we will proceed easterly. We will walk all night – and lie up in the day. I reckon it's forty miles to Gretford – but fifty or sixty as we'll go. And I think we'll stand a better chance about there than here. We'll have friends there – and we can hide in the woods there as well as here. We'll get fed – and we can hide. That's all we can think of for the moment. Slight thing that worries me is – what about the grub?"

Eli put his hand inside his tattered old jacket and pulled out two pheasants! And Dike pulled out of his pocket another.

"We weren't born yesterday," Dike said. Dike said he had picked his up during a drive. Eli had actually had a strong enough poacher's instinct to nick his after we had killed the captain, when he was picking the gun up. I hadn't seen him.

We did not rest long. I had no doubt whatever that the hunt was well and truly up by now. We started walking as quickly and as quietly as we could through the woods – roughly in an easterly direction. It was terribly dark – but we could just make the lines of the trees out. I cheered myself with thinking that the military police, and other uniformed riffraff, were all townsmen, and pretty inept. They had cars – but the forest was vast. They were not over-manned; the guard was thin on the ground anyway. They would not spare many men. Their communications were bad. They would realise that their chances of catching us were remote: they would be inclined to cut their losses and concentrate on keeping the rest of the prisoners in.

It is a strange feeling, being a fugitive.

There is the elation of walking fast in the cold air – one's heart and lungs work at full pressure: there is a feeling of intense physical well-being. There is the high sense of excitement. But there is a terrible foreboding too. You expect to meet them at every turn. The forest is full of menace. You probably exaggerate your peril. You keep trying to reassure yourself: to number all the factors in your favour. But the menace behind the next tree is still there.

We came out of the forest – into woodland and park country. We crossed many roads and lanes. My vaunted knowledge of the country was of no avail: I had no idea where I was. We kept our course by the wind – and later by the stars, that began to show in the windy sky.

By first dawn we could see that we were in fairly open country. Big fields with hedges but no ditches: that light, sandy land required no draining.

Over on the right was a big wood: we could just make it out in that early light before dawn. We headed for it, keeping along a hedge in a field. It was mixed with a young plantation of larch and pine and with hard-wood, mostly beech, coppice around the edge. We made our way through it – it was thick-going in parts – much overgrown with brambles. We found a field on the other side – no sign of a road anywhere, nor any house. We went back to where we judged was the middle of the wood, and there cast ourselves down.

We were not thirsty: we had found a mere and a couple of ponds and had quenched our thirst at them. We were tired and hungry.

"We'll light a fire," I said, "and cook a bird before it gets light enough for them to see our smoke." Then – "Hell! Have we got any matches?" We had. Both Dike and Eli had some. I collected some dry larch twigs while Eli plucked a pheasant, and we made a fire. A very small fire, with not much smoke. We cut the pheasant up (I had my knife still) and roasted it in bits on pointed sticks. It was tough – but Dike said: "Tougher if there wasn't any."

Eli strode off and found a wet patch, with a small muddy pond, at the end of the wood. We went and quenched our thirsts. We then went back to our camping place and prepared for the day.

I gave Eli a lesson in the automatic carbine. I then told them to rest, while I stood guard.

We cut thick mats of dead bracken with our knives (there was plenty of bracken in the clearings), and snuggled down like puppies in straw. I wandered to each edge of the wood in turn, and looked out over the cold April landscape. The fields were enormous – and quite empty. Some snow still lay, in the shade. The sun came out, but was low and had no heat. I was extremely cold. I could make out no landmark – see no people. I stuck it as long as I could – and then returned to my companions – woke Dike up – and took his place in the warm, dry bracken. The last thing that I remembered was Dike heaping another double-armful on me that he had cut – and then I went to sleep.

Chapter Ten

by Dike Randle

(Recorded by Eliza Keeble.)

Goo to hell Eliza if I see why ol' Bob shouldn't write it all down hisself – he's a lettered man and he saw it all same as myself. He say he's too busy getting his onions in – well what about my onions? But there, he's still the captain and what he say goes. I reckon if he asked me to jump in the sea I'd do it. So here goes.

I remember well that first day after we scarpered from the prison camp. Blast that was cold! The oud bracken helped – we'd ha' died without it but that was still some cold!

Oud Eli first wuk up and he say: "Come on Skip – let's get a'gooin'. Don't we'll freeze to dead!"

We crawled out. I was that stiff! I fared as I could hardly stand up. There was two dead rabbits hanging in a tree. I put 'em down to Eli. I knew that as long as we were along of him we 'ouldn't starve. I reckon that he'd find a bunny or a long-tail at the North Pole!

So – no tea nor naathin' – we set out eastward – long afore it was properly dark. Eli and I soon had confidence in old Bob. He were a master one for tactics. He kept us well in cover and we all had to hev a good look up and down afore ever we crossed any open space or a road. Then – thank God we come to this old farmhouse.

Now o' course most of the farmhouses at that time weren't inhabited by farmers. The land had all been bought up by these big companies, like London Farming, and the houses sold off to private gentry. This here farmhouse was inhabited by two skeletons. From the signs we could see as there'd bin a fight. There was shots in the door. I reckon some looters had come – the people in the house had tried to stop 'em – had shotguns I shouldn't wonder – but that hadn't worked. The looters took all the food but – thank God – they missed a packet of tea.

By God that was the best thing we could've found. You youngsters like you Eliza can't imagine what it was to be really hooked on tea, and we was, and then just to miss it. Right up to the time Bob was taken off we had had tea because Mick Miller had brought cases of it in his barge. But thaas the one thing we whully missed.

And dam' there was a calor-gas stove and gas in the bottle and a full rain butt by the back door. We drank tea until it came out of our ears!

Then we found up some spuds in the garden, volunteers what had kept a'growing and Eli appoints himself chief cook and bottle-washer and we has a duzzy great spread of spuds and pheasant and rabbit and we didn't take a lot of harm.

Upstairs blast if there wasn't blankets on the beds and we lay down and slept like birds.

Oud Eli was fair worried about his missus. He's a rum boy oud Eli. Thank God he can't read do he'd read what I'm a' sayin' about him. But in some ways he was a notorious character. That didn't do to rile him. I've sin him split a man's jaw – bust his jaw so he was in hospital for a few weeks. He was easy upset. But with oud Mary his oud wife – he thought the world of her. They'd fight togither mind. But he'd always let her win. They was always coming along to *The Barge Inn* and they'd fight togither, and argue, and the oud woman'd hit him, and he fared to be scared stiff of her. Blast gel he could've felled her with his little finger – she was only a scrap of a thing. Then they'd git up and dance! Goo to hell they could dance! Real oud steppers they was – the real oud Gypsy step-dance. So long as someone'd play the melodeon for 'em, or the mouth organ, or even just start a'hitting on the oud tin tray – that was enough!

But Eli wouldn't stop worrying about the oud gel. "Go to sleep Eli and get some rest!" say Bob. And I tell him the same. But he lies a'worrying like an oud ewe lost her lamb.

One thing we found there was maps. Whoever'd owned the place had plenty of 'em and the looters hadn't bothered with 'em. They wouldn't ha known which way up one was, I don't suppose. Bob decided we was to skirt north of Diss. So we loaded up with blankets, and maps, and this tea, and a small pressure cooker, and one or two other odds and ends, and off we goes, as soon as it gets dark, and skirts round Diss and crosses the Waveney back into silly Suffolk again and heads south-east. Eli was in a master hurry to find if his oud woman was safe and sound.

We walked all night. Just before dawn we hear a dog barking and see a fire a'glimmering. "We'll skirt round that lot," say Bob. But no – Eli say: "Do you come along o' me and keep quiet a bit."

So he leads us to the edge of this wood and there was a crowd of Gypsies sittin' round a fire. They had a lot of oud lorry chassis they'd pulled the engines out of and fixed shafts on so's they could be pulled by horses. There was a horse tethered nearby and several grown ups and children. Big high fire – that looked right cheerful.

"Hold you on a moment," says Eli. "Do you stay here a mo." And he walks forard towards these didikois.

Well the oud dogs kick up such a clamour it's like all hell let loose. The men tells 'em to shut up and Eli strides up to 'em and speaks to 'em and I reckon he uses some of their Gypsy language. We'd allus known Eli had more'n a little Gyppo in him but he kept it quiet like. But now no doubt he come out with it.

He speaks to 'em a few minutes and then shouts to us. "Come you in!" he say.

In we goes and these here people welcomes us, and they got

tea, and some bacon and bread – blast they didn't seem to goo
short o'much. "Let the gentlemen sit by the fire!" says this oud
woman. "And you chavvis," she said to the children. "Git out o'
the gentlemens' faces will you! What sort o' manners you got?"

We doesn't tell 'em we're on the run. I think they has a good
guess though. They give us some dam' good information about
the army. Bob he pulls out the map and Eli questions 'em and
Bob marks a lot of army positions.

I whully likes these Gypsies. They seemed all right to me.
I reckoned that whoever else survived in England these lot
would. They knew how to look after theirselves. There was one
young fellow we met there we were to see more of later on an'
that's oud Bert Herron and he come into this book we're a'doing
later on.

Well Eli won't rest and so we says goodbye and on we goes
daylight and all. Some time that afternoon we hears motor
engines. We're getting near Willingham," say Bob. "I reckon
we'd better hide up 'til dark, there's no point taking any risks."

"I'm a'gooin to goo on now!" say Eli.

"Look Eli – you do as oud Bob say," I tell him. "He's the
cap'n. If we all sticks togither and does what Bob say we 'on't
take a lot o' harm. He's bin a souldier and he know what he's
a'doin' of."

"Look Eli – if you get caught they'll shoot you as soon as look
at you!" say Bob. "Don't be a fool now. You're a dam' site more
use to Mary alive than you are dead."

Eli listened to reason and we hide up under some straw in a hay
barn. Eli'd listen to Bob. Bob was the only man I know as could
make Eli do what he wanted him to do.

We were off at dusk and we came to the Gret about midnight. I
knew this oud boy what kept a gun punt about a mile upstream of
Yeldham Ferry. I thought he wouldn't mind if we borrowed it,
particularly if he didn't know. We found it well hid in some
reeds – that was a hell of a job to find it. We crossed the river
and hid it up well the other side. We walked on upstream to
Sibford Maltings. Thass where the pair on 'em expected to find

their wives.

Eli's house was right near there and he wanted to goo there and look for Mary. Bob pointed out she was probably shut up in the Maltings the same as we knew Bob's family was.

Bob know'd all about these here Maltings because he'd been a'helping his wife to convert them into a hospital and refugee camp. We follows him in, all three of us.

I'll never forget what followed. That'll stay with me all my life. As we went in my heart was in my mouth – it was for all of us, I do believe. Eli was like someone crazed.

Bob leads the way into one of the big oud malting floors which had hundreds of sleeping people. Funny – like a nightmare it was. But we see a light in there. There was a hurricane lamp on a table. By the table sits this nurse – with her head down on her arms.

We steps over all these sleeping people and goes to the gel – and Bob shakes her shoulder. That was Elsie Band! We'd all known her from a child – in fact she was my niece. "Elsie!" said Bob. "It's me – Bob Hurlock! Don't be frightened! We shan't hurt you!"

She looked up at us and she shruk! She shruk right out and I couldn't blame her – we was a funny looking lot! We were slung about with guns and we looked like Mexican bandits.

"All right Elsie oud gel!" I comforts her. "We 'on't do you na harm. This is me – Dike Randle! Blast gel – don't you know your own uncle?"

She calmed down.

"Where's Mary – my missus?" Eli say to her. He fared right fierce.

"Eli!" she say. "Oh my God!" she kep' a' saying. "Oh my God!" She fare right distracted.

"Where's Mary?" shout Eli.

"Shut up Eli!" say Bob. "You'll wake the whul dam' lot of 'em!"

"I don't care who I wake – where's Mary?" he say.

Elsie stand up and look him in the eye. "Mary's gone," she

say. "She was here but she's gone. And Mr Hurlock your family's gone too. All of 'em. They was here but they've gone."

"Has she gone hoom?" say Eli.

"I don't think so," she say.

"Have they . . . have they . . ." Eli looked like a man crazed.

"Have they . . ." he kep' a'saying. He couldn't get it out.

"Mr Woolpit, I don't know," she say. "Some soudiers come and took 'em away. Your wife – Mr Hurlock – and the four kids. Thass all I can tell you."

She was as white as a sheet. She was a'shakin'! I felt right sorry for the little maather.

I look at Bob. He just stand there.

"Hev they shot 'em" Eli shouts. "Hev they shot 'em?" He's bellowing it out: "I don't know – I don't know!" say poor Elsie. That weren't her fault whatever they'd a'done.

"They just took 'em away. An officer and four soudiers. Just come, with a bit o' paper which they shew, and took 'em away."

"If they've . . . if they've . . . if they've . . ." shout Eli. He was like a madman. He stood there a'gasping for breath. He looked wicked – I tell you Eliza I stood there downright a'feared of him. He had murder in his eyes. Then suddenly he just collapsed. Like he'd hed the stuffin' taken out of him. He fell on his knees – put his arms on the table and dropped his head on 'em and he wept! Dam' great sobs – I was right scared – I thought he was a'goin' to die. I never heard such sobs – in my born days I never heard a man sob like it. It racked him!

Oud Bob jest stood there like he was made of wood. He jest stood there. He didn't move.

And all the sleeping people – they was a'wakin' up. They was a'sittin' up and there was babbies a'cryin' and men a'getting up. There was women a'shoutin' what's the matter and a hell of a hullabaloo a'building up.

"Bob!" I shouts. "We got to get out of here!"

Bob don't answer and he don't move. He stand there like he was made of wood.

I goes right up to him and grabs him by the arm and shouts in his ear: "Bob we got to goo! Thass dangerous! We got to git out!"

Bob nods his head. "Yes Dike," he say, right quiet like. "Yes Dike. Yes – we got to go."

Then I thinks – how are we goin' to git Eli away. I knelt down beside the poor oud boy. "Eli!" I say. "Eli! Eli we got to goo! The soudiers'll be here any minute. We got to goo!"

He just went on with these huge gret racking sobs.

"Eli!" I shouts. "They're all a'wakin' up here – we got to goo!" He turns to me and yells: "Goo where you fucking well like! Leave me alone!"

Bob kneels down on the other side of him. He speaks to him right quietly like – like he was talking to a child.

"Eli – Mary may well be alive," he say. "They may have taken her away somewhere else. We must go and find her!"

"They've shot her – the sods have shot her!" he shout.

Poor oud Bob kep' quiet for a bit then he say: "Eli – if they hev shot her – will you let 'em git away with it?"

Eli hauled hisself onto his feet. His gun had fallen on the floor – he picked it up and slung it on his shou'der. His eyes looked some terrible in the light of that lamp – there was other lights bein' lit then too. I tell you I was frightened of him.

"I swear by God!" he say. "I swear by my God above that I will not rest until I've killed every fucking soldier in this land. I'll smash the bloody lot of 'em!"

"Right then – follow me," say Bob, quiet like. And he walks away towards the door. He never looked back once Bob didn't. He didn't look back to see if we was a'followin'. I believe thass why we all used to follow the oud boy. He walked off as if he knew we was a'goin' to follow him. He never doubted it. He never looked back oud Bob didn't. And follow him we did. He didn't hev to look back.

Chapter Eleven

by Bob Hurlock

I sat down on the pine needles and tried to think.

Was there any use in trying to find our wives? Where would they be? Almost certainly dead, anyway. If not they would be in Willingham Castle. There was no possible way of getting them out of there. Either they were dead, or they were in the Castle. If the latter, to try to rescue them might precipitate their being shot. Certainly it would end in our being shot.

And I realised, quite suddenly and very strongly, that I did not want to be shot. Above all I did not want to be killed. I wanted to live as long as I possibly could – and all the while that I lived I wanted to hunt down and kill the people who had destroyed my family.

I wasn't worrying about England any more. In the first days I had had all sorts of plans – of trying to help to make our countryside a pleasant and happy place to live in again. Now I didn't care a damn. I knew that some horrible sort of feudal fascism was going to grow up. It was bigger than I was but I would go on preying on it as long as I lived, and I was very anxious to live a long time. Just for one purpose.

Eli had sunk down at the foot of his tree, and he was still sobbing with terrible choking gasps. We let him be. I got up and paced about. Dike just sat down and waited.

After about half an hour I went to Eli and said: "Eli – get up."

"Get up Eli! Get up!"

He slowly got to his feet.

"Now then Eli," I said. "Do you remember hitting that man over the head with the axe-helve?"

"Yes."

"Do you remember shooting the other man with the shot gun?"

"Yes."

"Do you want them to be the last you serve like that?"

He was silent for a moment, then burst out: "By God I swear by Christ I'll kill as many of the sods as I can lay my hands on!"

"Right then," I said. "You've got to forget about Mary. You've just got to forget all about her. We've only one thing to do now. Do you agree Dike?"

"You don't want to worry about me," said Dike.

"From now on we live in the forest and we hunt those buggers down."

Dike said he knew of a forest hut right in the middle of one of the big plantations, where we would be safe for the night. We got to it after about an hour, broke the lock, and went in. It was cold, so we lit a fire. There were plenty of wood chippings about. We took turns to watch, while two of us slept through the day.

"Do you know," said Dike, when we all woke up. "I'm in a mind to look in at *The Barge* tonight."

I thought about it, and finally decided that it might be a good idea.

We hung about until dark, playing dominoes (for Dike had pocketed the set that we had found at the last farmhouse), cooking our last pheasant and eating it, and making a long journey to an emergency water tank, one of the deep pools provided by the Forestry Commission for fire engines to draw from in the event of a fire. Eli walked about in a kind of daze, but he did whatever we told him. He did not talk much.

After dark we walked through the forest towards Yeldham Ferry. There was a light on in the pub, and we could hear people talking. Dike crept to the window and looked through – then came back to us and said: "There's no-one in there we don't know, and no-one we can't trust I reckon."

"Come on," I said. "Let's go in."

We walked into the yard at the back, and in through the back door. I led the way, then Eli, then Dike.

As I entered the crowded tap-room a silence fell on the company. The game of darts stopped in mid throw.

The three of us walked up to the bar. Our automatics were slung over our shoulders.

"Three pints please," I said to Mrs Denny, who stood behind the bar.

"We can't get the malt now," she said. "We're drinking this. Sugar beet wine we call it. Made from sugar beet. Thass better'n nothing but that in't a mucher."

She poured us out three glasses.

We took them up. "Good health!" I said.

"Thass nice to see you!" said one man. And several others concurred. The silence was broken, and there was much friendly greeting and back-slapping. "Go to hell I thought you'd gone to Siberia together!"

"We got something to say to you lot," said Dike. "Cap'n – tell 'em what we got to say."

I told them what had happened to Eli's wife and my wife and family. They all knew anyway. I could see by their faces that they knew the worst.

"Now then," I said, "you listen here. That army as they call themselves are no more the government of England than my cat. They're a crowd of riff-raff from the Midlands. They've no more right in East Anglia than the Russians would have – or the Yanks did have. You people have allowed yourselves to be trodden on since William the Conqueror. You've – well we've – I was as much to blame as anybody – we let those bastards in far too easily. We were all afraid of doing a bit of work, that was half the trouble. Just sit back and let "them" organise things – let "them" supply the diesel for the tractors and do the farming. Now they're here. But believe me – they're not here to stay.

We're going to kick them out. We've shot some already – and we're going to shoot a hell of a lot more. It's time you people – the real people of East Anglia – owned your own country for a change. For two thousand years you've been refugees in your own country. First you've had the Normans – then the aristocrats and feudal barons – then the cotton manufacturers and their blasted pheasants – now you've got this lot. And you're going to kick them out and own your own land for a change."

There was a short silence. Then a man named Bill Keeble said: "I don't rightly see how we can do it, Captain. There's not a man here who don't agree with you – leastways about this last lot – but there's hundreds on 'em at Willingham, they say there's a whole battalion – armoured cars – tanks – the lot. Here there's quite a few. I don't see what we can do about 'em."

"Maybe you can't do much yet," I said. "The three of us here are going to take to the forest. If there's anyone among you got the guts he can join us. Only thing is wives and families. It's a job for bachelors to start with . . ."

"I'll come!" said a young man named Phil Everard.

"Put me down too!" said Doug Burrows.

"Well we'll hole up in the forest – and we'll prey on these buggers. The rest of you'll play the game and give us food. We'll get guns off the soldiers we kill . . ."

"We've got several weapons," said someone. "There's a lot hidden away they don't know naathin' about."

"Good. Bring 'em along."

"Tell you what," said someone. "People are getting right fed up with this army. There's people all about here'd do anything to get shut on 'em. They've taken to pinching girls now. There's rape and all sorts of nonsense going on."

"We'd all help you Bob – if we thought we could. We'll do whatever we can. But them as has got wives and families – we can't just abandon 'em you know. And the buggers'll kill 'em do we go off and leave 'em. As you know."

"Well we mustn't hang about here too long," I said. "We'll go back to the forest now."

"Have another glass before you go!" said Mrs Denny.

"I won't say no although that's rum old stuff. A couple of you might come with us and we can show you where we'll be in case anybody wants to join us, or bring us anything."

"There's one thing," said Bill Keeble, looking round at the company. "If anybody here gives these chaps away, or give anyone information about 'em, that'll be their lot. Thass straight now! That'll be the end on 'em!"

And there was a general murmur of agreement.

And when we left the pub there were six of us, for another young bachelor called Tom had decided to come with us, as well as Phil Everard and Doug Burrows. Tom Jay was a notorious poacher and a good man in the woods.

We led them back to our forest hut, and there we had a conference.

"You go home now you know where we are," I said, "and come back, if you like, with weapons."

"I know where there's a Carl Gustav hid." That was a very powerful recoil-less projector.

"Bring the beggar," said Eli.

"Tell you what," said Dike. "When you come back here – whistle *The Larks*. Then we shall know who you are. Otherwise you might get a burst through your guts . . ." *The Larks* was an old song sung thereabouts; no outsiders would know it: 'The Larks they sang melodious at the dawning of the day.'

"I reckon I could get here with that bazooka by tomorrow morning," said Tom. "That's not far from here."

"You really want to join us then?"

"Definitely. There in't no future in that present carry-on. Life's not worth living na more. If it weren't for what we poach and scrounge there wouldn't be na grub. And there won't be for what I can see on it. They don't farm the land they do work – they only scratch about." The other two agreed.

"Right," I said. "Off you go. The three of you. Get the recoilless-rifle – bazooka or whatever it is – and come back here."

I explained to Dike and Eli that we ought to strike, and strike soon. Show the populace that we really could do something. We would soon get weary of merely sitting in the forest getting cold.

The three boys came back just before dawn. They had a fourth with them and the promised Carl Gustav, or bazooka as we called it. I hadn't seen one of these before; we didn't have them during my service. It was a heavy tube which one man held over his shoulder and aimed at the target while the other loaded it and fired. The recoil shot out the back, and out of the front came a hollow-charge, eighty-four millimetre shell. It would blow a tank to a stand-still. It was fired mechanically so there was no battery to worry about. Each boy also had an automatic rifle. Dugdale had done his terriers well. And the boys carried between them twenty shells for the bazooka.

We spent part of the day practising with each other in the use of weapons – without firing them of course. At dark we set off through the forest towards Gretford.

We had decided to start on *The Crown Hotel*. All the "officers" in our district lived there, and we had had information on which bedroom Dobson's was.

The forest led to within a mile of Gretford, and at the edge of it we sat down and concealed ourselves near the road, while two of the young recruits nipped across it to shin up and cut the telephone wires. Then we waited.

No less than three military cars or trucks came by, and a motor cycle. There was a temptation to fire at them, which we resisted. The army were not being sparing with whatever petrol there remained in the country, even though the Fenlands had had to be drowned.

We waited until after midnight; then moved in single file – across the road, along hedges and spinneys that we knew – into the little town itself.

We climbed over a brick wall into the garden of a very large house (which had been turned into a hostel) from the front of which we could find a position that gave us a good view of the front of *The Crown Hotel*. The range was about forty yards.

"That's Charlie-boy's room," whispered Tom, the boy with the bazooka. The room indicated still had a light on in it (we could hear the charging engine) all the rest of the town was in darkness, and apparently asleep.

I was annoyed because my companions seemed to be making too much noise. It was a still, clear, frosty night, with no moon, and, except for the charging engine, you could hear a pin drop. Tom banged the bazooka against the brick wall, somebody smashed a glass cloche.

"Shhhh!" said Dike.

Just then – a figure appeared in the lighted window. The casement window had been open a few inches on top – now it was flung half open.

"Fire!" I whispered.

A terrific report – a blinding flash – the whole of the front of the black shape of the hotel seemed to light up, and then darkness. The light in the room was out.

"Now the other window!"

The boys worked the bazooka quickly and well. Shell after shell was slammed into the front of the hotel – six in all.

"Now scram!" I said.

We had arranged that each should take his own line back to an arranged hideout by a road junction – where the main road from Gretford split three ways: to go to Blackstream, Randersfield and Sibford.

Eli and I kept together – to my amazement Eli was roaring with laughter – and we ran as fast as we could, keeping to hedges, until we got into the woods – my woods – of Cragpit Farm. From there we kept on until we reached the pine forest, and through this we walked until we came to the rendezvous. We were very blown, and flopped on the ground for a few minutes to recover our breath. We had not heard anything of the enemy for some time, but now we heard a motor-cycle engine roaring along the road from Gretford.

We watched the headlights illuminate the pine trees above us. The lights flashed round, the roar of the engine got louder, then suddenly, as if the motor-cycle engine had gone mad, there was another crackling, superimposed on it. Then there was a crash – and silence. I realised that the other noise had been the noise of an automatic rifle.

Eli and I crept forward and I softly whistled *The Larks*. The answering bar came back.

The place where we had chosen to meet was an old quarry, right by the cross roads. It had been planted with poplars, but was thickly grown with bracken and brambles, and I thought it would make a good hiding place for an ambush. Apparently it had.

Dike and a fourth boy to join us, named Billy, were there. They were dragging a dead man and a motor-cycle out of the road. They pulled both down into the quarry, and then Dike, Eli and Billy lay on guard while I went over the body.

I found a letter and put it in my pocket.

Soon we heard *The Larks* again, and the others arrived. I put them in position to watch the road.

We could hear car and lorry engines moving about near Gretford. Then the noise of something coming our way reached us. Some vehicle coming from Gretford direction. The headlights swept past us as it turned the corner a couple of hundred yards from us – and we could judge that it was a lorry approaching. The headlights came on – I heard the roar of the bazooka to one side of me – but the lorry did not stop. A miss. Indeed it was hard to aim in that poor light. But we all opened up with our automatics – the headlights swung round – blinding us – there was a crash as the lorry hit a tree by the edge of our quarry and came to a dead stop. Against the night sky we could see it was full of men. They were very near us. We all fired at them until our magazines were empty and then put new ones in.

It was some time before there was any return fire, and then it was very scattered and wild. Then we could hear running footsteps receding down the road towards Gretford.

"Stop firing!" I shouted, and there was silence.

I could hear a man groaning in the truck. It was very dark and

I could just see the square bulk of the lorry. I didn't know what to do. I didn't want to get anybody wounded, and I was afraid that if we charged the lorry someone lying inside it might easily have that much kick left. I thought of the arms and ammunition that were probably in the lorry – but then I thought of the embarrassment of a wounded comrade in that forest. And we were not short of weapons.

"Let's go for 'em!" said Eli, beside me.

"No," I said. I crawled to where Billy was lying. "You're a lorry driver," I said. "Do you know where the fuel tank is?"

"Ay."

"Creep up, very gently, and put a short burst into it." He did so. We could hear the fuel running out on the ground. But how to light it? But Eli was equal to this. He picked up an old newspaper which had been lying in the brambles beside the road (it had once been a favourite picnic spot), crawled up to the lorry – while we gave short bursts of covering fire – lit the paper with a match and ran up and placed it under the tank.

There was a flare – we were suddenly horribly conscious that we were no longer hidden by the dark.

"Scram!" I shouted, and we all turned and ran – into the forest. We could hear screams coming from behind us – where the flames were.

We were all safely back at the forest hut before dawn, and nobody had got hurt. I opened the letter that I had found on the motor cyclist and read it out loud by the light of our fire. It said:

TO: 4th Bn.	FROM: B Coy.
DATE: 24 APRIL	TIME: 0330 hrs.

MAJOR DOBSON AND TWO OFFICERS KILLED
BY SURPRISE BAZOOKA ATTACK ON HQ.
UNKNOWN ATTACKERS HAVE DISAPPEARED.
PRESUMABLY INTO FOREST.

JOHN SYMES Lt.

"Let 'em sort that one out," said Eli. "And thass only a start!"

Chapter Twelve

by Lieutenant-Colonel John Nightingale

It is strange that the man who asked me to write of my experiences for inclusion in a book, the first book to be published, in this part of England at least, since the CRISIS was, a few years ago, my worst enemy. In fact if I could have shot him I certainly would have done so (I spent over a year just trying to do that) and if he could have shot me he would have done so too. Which leads me to question the whole business of war, since the world's beginning, and to question my profession.

For, until my career ended abruptly at the beginning of last year, I was a professional soldier. Nothing could have been more conventional than my army experience and I will certainly not bore the reader with it here. Suffice to say that it started in the officer cadet corps of my public school, went through Sandhurst, failed to make Staff College, and took me back to the dizzy height of Lieutenant-Colonel. What do I call myself now: "Colonel (retired)"? "Colonel (failed)" would be more like it. Or "Colonel (run-away)" perhaps.

The experience of my whole generation of officers in the British Army was to find that our training, and the emphasis of our endeavours, shifted slowly but inevitably from what we thought the proper business of a soldier was – to fight an armed enemy – to what our superiors like to call "action in aid of civil power". I was too young to have taken part in the Second World War, or Malaya and Korea, and the only action I saw, if you could call it action, was in Northern Ireland. The latter was not to my taste, nor was it to the taste of any other soldier. Whatever we might have thought of the IRA I don't think many of us had much admiration for the other side either: the bowler-hatted, drum-beating, bombastic Orangemen. My sympathies were all for the ordinary people there, catholic or protestant, who just wanted to get on with their lives and live in peace.

But undoubtedly the powers that controlled us looked upon Ireland as a training ground for the sort of action we would be likely to be wanted for in the future, just as the commanders of the old Indian Army looked upon the North-West Frontier Province as an ideal training ground for the troops whose job it was to hold India for the British Raj. A live enemy, always there and never to be beaten, but which could never beat you, is ideal for training generations of troops.

We thought less and less of fighting a conventional army and more and more of fighting terrorist groups, or civil disobedience people, or strikers, or revolutionaries among our own people. This policy seemed to come down to us from Staff College. Chaps would graduate from there and come to take over divisions, and seem to think of nothing else but how to conduct campaigns against British people in our own cities. I did not like this; few soldiers did, but if you are a professional soldier you do not question the orders that come down to you from above. I did toy with the idea of getting out of it though, many times. I thought of chucking up my commission and getting a farm. But what did I know of farming? And with land at ten thousand pounds an acre it seemed a bit silly to forego my pension. Funny thing – I am a farm labourer now and damned lucky to be one.

Anyway – this book I have been asked to contribute to starts its action during those awful days in December when everything fell to pieces.

I always thought the end of it all would be an outbreak of nuclear war. The British Isles was really nothing but an unsinkable aircraft carrier for the Americans, and war between the latter and the Russians seemed inevitable. I had imagined

Armageddon in the form of a shower of ballistic missiles with nuclear war heads and the destruction, in just a few minutes, of all our cities. It did not happen that way. There was no nuclear war. There was no war.

There was just this progressive breakdown in the morale of all the British people – and the people of the rest of the Western world in fact. Since the CRASH we have had very little news from outside England but what little news we have had points to an astonishing similarity between what happened here and what happened in every highly industrialised country of the West, both in Europe and in America. Only the little countries, such as Ireland and Denmark, seemed to escape.

All during the 1990s the Western world had to adapt itself to higher and higher oil, gas, and coal prices, greater and greater inflation, dearer and dearer and scarcer and scarcer raw materials from what in those days we gaily called the Third World. But adapt we did and life went on pretty much the same for most of the decade except there was more and more unemployment. Why, until the beginning of the century motor cars were still increasing – even when the price of petrol hit ten pounds a litre. People just would not give up their motoring – I believe they would have starved first. The motor car was a wonderful thing; it made the puniest little man into a centaur and gave him a feeling of effortless power. True, all during the decade life got worse for city people. Things they needed got scarcer, the very poor began to suffer very badly (the deaths of old people from cold in every big city mounted steadily as the decade wore on), unemployment became the norm for many people – and for chaps who were by no means lazy either – and young fellows leaving school found it very hard to get a job. But the State supported them, albeit at a lower and lower level of subsistence. An increasing number of young people left the cities and tried to get a foothold in the country, but the policy of the government was to discourage this and they had a very tough time of it. Land prices worked steadily upwards until only rich Arabs and other foreigners, or big finance companies, could afford to buy it at all. True the

planning laws more or less collapsed in about 20 - - so many
people were just defying them and building houses on their bits
of land regardless of the laws which were impossible to enforce.
But, by and large, the back-to-the-land movement was never an
important factor.

Then came that awful winter.

I was at Camberley at the time and the battalion I commanded,
the First Mercian Rifles, had just come back from Germany.
Most of my chaps were on leave and the battalion, which had
been whittled down to a miserable establishment of five hundred
men anyway, was a mere skeleton. It was a shocking winter. All
over the northern hemisphere apparently it was the same: the
coldest winter since 1963. We were all right in the army, of
course. At least we had oil and gas to keep our quarters warm
and plenty of food. But the country as a whole was in a state of
crisis.

By then everything had deteriorated in most western countries
anyway. A constant series of strikes had weakened industry,
damaged the railway system, allowed roads to go into decay.
Government spending, although it rocketed every year, never
seemed enough to keep the country in proper order. Vast sums,
of course, went on the nuclear power industry but, in spite of the
fact that there were forty nuclear power stations on stream during
that winter, they never really came up to expectations. There
were the accidents all the time. All over the world there were
nuclear accidents in those days and each one put up the price of
electricity as the industry was forced to take ever more expensive
and stringent precautions. Every time there was a bad accident
public confidence was shaken, and my battalion was called out to
disperse demonstrators in several parts of the country. The
nuclear police had to be added to every year until it became
almost a rival army.

Then there came the Fell-a-Pylon Campaign. Somebody found
you could cut through the slender legs of an electricity pylon
with an ordinary hacksaw in a couple of hours and the anti-
nuclear extremists started doing this with a right good will. And

nobody could stop them. We were sending army patrols all over the country looking for them but it was a complete wild-goose chase. Lines of pylons went over all the most remote country – through great areas of Forestry Commission forests and high mountains and it just was not possible to guard every mile of it. The police managed to prosecute a few people – generally because they traced the tyre marks of their cars – but I don't believe they ever actually caught anybody red-handed on the job. After the melt down of a nuclear power station in France, which made it necessary to evacuate the Channel Islands, and then the bad release of radioactivity at Sellafield, and the disaster at Dungeness, and the odd disaster in other parts of the world (the South Americans didn't seem very good at looking after these things) the anti-nukes got very strong. I would have been one of them, I think, if I hadn't been in the army. But the government was very obstinate about going on with the nuclear industry.

And terrorism everywhere was getting out of hand. There was the anti-computer campaign for example. As the decade wore on the government and the police, and particularly the Nuclear Police Force, fed more and more information about all of us into their computers. This annoyed some people, including me I have to admit. One day somebody got the brilliant idea of hijacking a large petrol road tanker, driving it to the building in Westminster which was said to house the most powerful computer in the world, and simply poking the hose through the foam inlet of the building. Everybody thought they were simply delivering heating oil and a policeman actually came up and stood there directing the traffic. At the appropriate moment the terrorists inserted an inflammatory device called a "tar baby", got quietly into a little car that was waiting for them, and drove away. The road tanker went on merrily pouring several thousand gallons of petrol into the building until it – and the building – and the most powerful computer in the world – blew up.

And with all this, by that terrible cold winter of 20 - -, the country was in no state to withstand a crisis. But a crisis there was to be. The North Sea was still yielding some oil then, although the natural gas was finished. The Government had realised that the end of the road for North Sea oil was a bit too near and were stringently trying to control its production. Worse they had halted, for several years, new exploration. And then came the Persian Gulf crisis – right on top of the Mexican Revolution, and the cat was really among the pigeons.

The United States went down first of course. Food production had fallen dramatically there during the previous decade, as the country, completely hooked on oil-derived chemicals to grow crops, had less and less chemicals to grow them with. North America still had food enough for its own population; but nobody had realised that it might one day be impossible to get the food to the consumers! The ordinary workings of the market had insured that every commodity was carried the maximum distance. Wheat would be transported hundreds of miles to the mills, milled, and the flour transported hundreds of miles back again. I didn't take much interest in those sort of things then but I have had all this explained to me now.

And suddenly there was no "gas", as the Americans called petrol. New York, Chicago, all the big cities began to run short of food simultaneously. And not only food: fuel for heating too. In America nuclear development had run into even more trouble than it had in England. America was more of a democracy in some ways than we were and the huge army of objectors there was able to bring the nuclear programme to a halt. In New York and Washington the lights went out and, in that terrible winter, people really did freeze in the dark. And they starved too.

This book is not to be about what happened in America, but what happened there certainly affected what happened here. Canada ceased to send a single shipment of wheat to England, of course, but that might not, by itself, have meant very much for a year or two. The City, of course, collapsed. There was a financial panic and run on the banks that made the 1920s collapse look like a picnic. The government simply put a stop to all industry and closed all banks. What fuel and power there was was to be preserved to keeping the people alive. Petrol rationing started in November immediately after the Mexican crisis; and owners of electric cars were no longer allowed to charge their batteries from the mains. By the beginning of December all private motoring was banned. All over the country people who held grain held on to it. Anybody could see the price of it could only rise and nobody but a fool would sell it. In any case the disruption that was happening to transport made it impossible to get the grain to the mills, or the flour to the big bread factories, or the bread to the people. At that time it was quite common for the big bread firms to carry bread, daily, a hundred miles to supply their customers. Bread rationing was introduced, but this became not very effective when there was no longer any bread to ration. In the end the Government was organising the sale of whole wheat and barley in the streets – with instructions as to how to grind it and bake bread with it!

In mid-November there was a general mobilisation of all troops and my battalion reformed at Camberley and we were immediately ordered to Birmingham. We proceeded in convoy up the M1 – the road was slippery as hell and there had been a lot of accidents – the road workers were on strike and the snow was not being cleared away – but we got through and the police met us and assigned us quarters in various parts of the city. We were to keep a low profile and were only to appear at all if asked to do so by the police.

I was not satisfied with our treatment and radioed our brigade headquarters, which was near Camberley, for orders. At first I was told to put up with it but in December my brigadier told me the whole country was under martial law and that I was simply to take over the government in Birmingham and the Black Country and if anybody, police or local government, got in my way I was to have them shot. I remember I could scarcely believe my ears when I heard this – it just did not seem possible in cosy law-abiding little England. Anyway I explained the position to the Chief of Police and to the Mayor and such members of the Corporation as were still around and they agreed to consider themselves under my orders. Indeed they had to.

There were attempts made by various groups in Birmingham to take over the government of the city. The leftists tried this and so did one or two other organisations. My orders from Brigade were to break up any such attempts and we did so. I am not sure now whether this was a wise policy. Perhaps more lives would have been saved if we had co-operated with some of these groups and allowed them to take over various parts of the city. Certainly the official city government was quite useless. They had nobody to give orders to and nobody would have taken any notice of their orders if they had. They seemed bereft of ideas completely. The Civil Defence organisation and one or two other groups were more use – they reported to me and did what I told them and also gave me advice. We moved into a tall building – a small skyscraper – by the Bullring. That was the centre of Birmingham. I liked it because radio transmission and reception were good from there. Until after Christmas we were able to keep the radio going in Birmingham from the Birmingham city centre; London faded out before Christmas. But everybody knew there was martial law in the land and that looters and others would be shot. This didn't stop people looting though – indeed there was nothing else they could do. My men were first set to guarding food convoys, and large wholesale foodstores, and any place where food or oil was stored. One anxiety was the cold stores, but one benefit of the cold winter was that the meat didn't rot.

It was staggering, the speed at which things broke down. We had not yet grasped one appalling situation when it was overwhelmed by another – and worse one. People were milling about the streets in Birmingham breaking into shops and stealing what they could. Mobs were marching to and fro – some going one way and some another – all shouting slogans but none of them apparently clear who they were supposed to be shouting at.

And everything broke down. Everything except the army that is, and the police. Orders got through to us but they were pointless orders and there seemed no possibility of obeying them. I remember a radio message from our divisional commander, who was in London by then, ordering me to bring the battalion immediately to London.

But by then my men were scattered all over Birmingham and the Black Country, the presence of each platoon was urgently required where it was because it was guarding food, or oil or petrol, and the one thing we all realised was that those things had to be guarded at any cost. We gave up all pretence that we were "aiding the civil power". There was no civil power. No telephones worked, there was no traffic, no-one was getting to office or city hall – every man and woman in the city was bent on one thing only – to find and stash away enough food. After the middle of December, I had to give the orders to shoot. If civilians did not stop immediately when challenged, the soldier was to shoot.

The police, which of course at that time were armed and with automatic weapons too, were under the same orders. I am ashamed to say there were occasions when police and army had small battles against each other: that is before the Chief of Police and I came to an understanding. They needed food too.

I cannot really describe what was happening to other people in those awful days – I only know what was happening to myself. There I was, with my headquarters in that horrible skyscraper absolutely appalled and shocked at what was going on. Above all, I decided, I must keep control over my command and keep control over most of it I did. Our Signals Platoon was marvellous, and every platoon and section of the battalion was kept in constant touch with headquarters. My officers and warrant officers and NCOs were first class. In spite of the fact that most of them came from Birmingham, or very near it, they stuck to their posts (I ordered company commanders to allow any man leave to go to his home if he wanted to provided that he came back within twenty four hours) and they obeyed orders. Of course very soon few of them had any homes to go to, to speak of, at all.

The electric supply cut off, the water system failed, ultimately only a disgusting brown liquid came from the taps. People began to get sick and people began to die. The temperature, by mid-January, was the lowest I have ever experienced, anywhere. Everywhere bands of men were breaking into houses, smashing out all the woodwork, and carrying the wood off to make fires. Birmingham had had quite a clean atmosphere before 20 - -, at least there was little smoke in it even if there was a lot of petrol fumes, but I remember, from the high windows of my headquarters, watching visibility slowly close in, as smoke from a million wood fires was belched into the atmosphere.

Because of our signals system, I was one of the few people in the city who had any idea of what was happening in the rest of the country. In London and Manchester an attempt was made by the army to prevent people from leaving the city. Troops were stationed on all exit roads to turn people back. Many people were shot, millions starved to death, and then the attempt to stop them was simply given up because it was impossible. In Birmingham the huge mob movements of the first few days died away quickly to leave, during the day at least, practically deserted streets. I think that applied in most cities. What was the good of marching about in a mob and shouting if nobody was there to listen to you? You didn't get a free dinner that way. I believe part of the desertion of our streets was caused by the fact that many people left Birmingham and streamed into the country to look for food.

Here I feel that I must justify myself a bit. You see, being in effective control of most of the stored food in the city, I was in a position to dish it out to whom I thought fit. Now it will be argued that I should have dished it out, but to whom? – the poor? – the starving? But everybody was in the way of starving.

I knew that the only way to stop complete and utter disaster with nobody left alive at all, was to keep my little army intact. So we got our rations as usual. I know that many of my men gave food away to starving people – many a boy from Birmingham in my lot gave half or more of his ration to an aged mother somewhere, or other relatives. But in the end – we had to survive. And, of course to put it at its lowest, we had the means to survive, didn't we? We soon found out where the grub was and we guarded it. At first we tried our best to distribute food in the streets, but when we realised how little there was to distribute, and saw how many people there were to distribute it to, and saw the awful scenes of riot and carnage that came when we tried to distribute it – as millions of people fought to be in the front of the queue – we had perforce to stop. It did no good and it just wasn't possible.

So, when the police force agreed to work under my command and the city government moved to our headquarters building, I saw to it that they at least got fed. Thus, for a time at least, many a fat councillor stayed fat.

One thing disturbed me and I tried to stop it, but could not. More and more of our men began to take girl friends, and keep them in their quarters, and feed them of course. Although this was against my ideas of discipline completely I had to turn a blind eye. I thought it all-important to keep the allegiance of my men, and I had an instinct that if I was to do this I must yield on this point. And, well, I might as well come clean right here at the start. I did save a young girl from starving too. When I found her sitting crying in the road I noticed that she was very young, very hungry, and extremely beautiful.

People were dying everywhere. The bitter cold, the lack of food, the terrible feeling of no hope that there was, did for millions. The Black Death must have been a picnic to what was happening in England then. At first the city authorities tried to organise body disposal but it became impossible. There was no stink at first – the weather was too cold. Bodies just did not rot. They lay about everywhere. The death-rate did one thing – it relieved the pressure and it began to make sense for me to send parties out to requisition food in the countryside. Gradually, with the help of the police and the authorities, we began to get things under control again. We had plenty of diesel; one of the first things we did was to take over all oil storage depots. No civilians could use vehicles anyway – if they had no permits they could be shot on sight. We began sending parties out – a section of men and three or four lorries – to requisition food from the surrounding country. We got the slaughterhouse working again, we set up milling capacity, got bread ovens going – with the greatly reduced numbers of people there were, by the middle of February, it began to be possible, and to make sense.

People began to hope again. A clean water supply became organised. The corpses began to be cleared up. They were flung into building excavations and bulldozed in. Both police and army were terribly over-stretched and we began to see that there must be recruiting. We began to take on able-bodied men and swear them into the police and the army. I had to beware of stretching the army too much or too quickly. I promoted my regular privates to NCOs and gave each one of them a sub-unit containing some regulars and a few new recruits. The latter were loyal enough – they realised that they were among the lucky ones. At least they would not starve.

There were several armed gangs of civilians about. These we simply shot on sight. Anybody who had a firearm of any sort was automatically shot – no questions asked. I intended to make sure that there was only one army in the area and that one to be under my command.

As for orders from on high – they simply ceased to arrive. We lost radio contact with London altogether. What happened there I just do not know. People began, I suppose, to be so busy just surviving in their own little pockets that they ceased to worry about anybody else. By the end of March I had given up all attempts to keep in touch with anybody else.

I found myself a little king in my area. My command included Wolverhampton, and all that conurbation in between. Coventry was controlled by another unit: a battalion of the Sherwood Foresters. Our patrols met theirs from time to time and we agreed on a boundary in the country between us. To the west we patrolled – and requisitioned – as far as the River Severn. Over that river the Welsh had taken over – it seemed that they had set up an autonomous state. They blew up all the bridges over the River Severn and made that their boundary. What they did over the other side of it, and how they fared, I do not know.

I really believe we did the best we could. I believe even more people would have died had we not been there. I am not ashamed of my actions. I obeyed my orders, as a soldier should, as long as I could. Then I acted with the best will in the world – I simply tried to do what was best. No man should ever be placed in the position I was in. No man should be asked to decide who should live and who should die – who should receive bread and who none. I did my best.

Chapter Thirteen

by Bob Hurlock

We dared not rest.

We realised that the enemy would set a very large force to surrounding and driving the local forests, and we would be best out of it. Reluctantly our half a dozen man army got to its feet and set off in the direction of the Gret. We crossed it where we had crossed it before, by means of the same punt. Then, in the rapidly growing daylight, we struck off north-westwards – holding on into another big block of pine forest, in the direction of Willingham itself. I reasoned that nine-tenths of the manpower of Willingham would spend the next day drawing Gretford District Woods.

Once well into the woods the other side of Bebbage, we holed up for a few hours. We all badly needed the rest.

We discussed another suitable target. I suggested the water tower that supplied water to Willingham. But young Billy had a better idea.

"You know them petrol tanks down in the dip this side of Willingham?"

"Yes but surely they haven't got petrol in 'em now?" I said.

"That they have – I've seen 'em filling of 'em. I've seen big road tankers pumping petrol and oil into 'em. I reckon thass where all the petrol in this district is kept."

"Lead on brother," I said.

We kept on again through the woods – as far as we could be

without coming into open country. Then we waited for dusk. The boys had brought some bread and some salt bacon, and this we ate. We were hungry, and very weary.

At nightfall we kept on our cautious way. The countryside was quite silent.

It was five miles of open country to the petrol tanks. I had fears for our retreat. However – the chance of such a target was too good to be missed.

The tanks appeared at first to be quite unguarded by men although we noticed that they had been surrounded by high barbed wire. We got to within twenty yards of this before we saw that there was, in fact, a sentry. Walking around inside the wire perimeter. We could only see him when he walked in front of one of the silver-painted tanks.

There were twelve tanks: we had thirteen bazooka shells. I whispered to Tom, the bazooka boy: "For God's sake make yourself comfortable – and lam one into the bottom of each of those tanks. Take your time over it."

Tom whispered: "That looks to me like the guard-room – by the gate."

"Poke one in there first then – just to wake 'em up. And the rest of you give 'em a short burst for good measure. Ready? All right then – fire!"

There was a crash of fire, and an explosion at the guard-room.

"Stop!" I said. "Now then Tom – go on boy – and for God's sake keep calm."

He was a good boy. He kept calm. He fired shells into seven tanks, though, before any petrol caught fire. Petrol doesn't catch light as easily as people think. But I suppose vapour from one of the tanks that he had holed was ignited by the flame from one of the bombs. At any rate – there was as sudden burst of flame. The heat immediately became unbearable.

"Keep on Tom!" I said. "Do the others!"

He fired at the other five. Some of the tanks may have been empty – we could not know. But at least there was enough juice there to make a fine blaze. As soon as Tom had fired his last bomb we scrammed. It was much too hot to bear.

And by daybreak we were hiding in a wood five miles to the north.

That day, I believe, was our day of real peril.

True, we later heard that almost the whole of Willingham garrison busied themselves that day in beating the woods near Gretford. Some breakdown in either their communications or their common sense failed to switch the pursuit farther north – to where we were. We heard lorries roaring along the roads near our wood from time to time, though, and once heard the sound of a whistle being blown not far away; presumably by the officer of a search party. We dared not leave our wood until darkness though. We lay crouching under bracken in a dell in a beech wood. In the open country we would have been far too conspicuous. But as soon as it got dark we crept out, along ditches and behind hedges, avoiding the roads and before light we had put twenty miles more ground behind us. We lay up for two days in a deserted farm house, getting our food by snaring rabbits and hares and digging up potatoes at night in the fields. We soon found that an essential piece of equipment was the head of a fork, strapped to somebody's back. For years after the CRASH potatoes still grew, as 'rogues', in the unharvested potato fields, and could be had for the digging. And that first year of course the crops were perfect: the bracken, nettles, spear grass and other perennials hadn't even begun to take over.

Reality, in this as in most things, upset all our theories. I am sure that if I had been given this book to read before the CRASH I would have punctuated my reading of it by shouting: "Nonsense! This wouldn't have happened – that wouldn't have happened – but this would have happened!" But, having lived through it all, I am in a position to tell you what actually did happen. I remember, soon after the CRASH came people in Gretford were green with fear because "plague" was going to break out! Of course no plague broke out. There was not enough people left in the country for it to break out amongst. The "sewage systems were going to break down" that was another cry. But why should they break down?

So we rested in our farmhouse, but kept a good guard. The enemy were thin on the ground; they had evidently visited practically every house in the countryside, to loot what they could find, but had not tried to settle. We knew they were inclined to keep together in large units. Willingham Castle was their headquarters for East Anglia; we knew there were some at Diss; and we judged, by their movements, that there was another lot somewhere near Lowestoft and Great Yarmouth.

We saw, and heard, several motorised parties travelling along the roads. Then, after our second night at the farmhouse, Eli came back from a foraging expedition to say that a platoon of enemy was searching the nearby village, house by house, and working its way towards us.

"Let's go and give 'em a surprise!" said he.

"No fear," I said. I gave orders to get out of the house – quick.

Someone wanted to improvise a booby-trap with a hand grenade but I said no. We were to leave no trace of ourselves and supposing an innocent person sprung it? We got out into the spinney at the back of the farmhouse and tried to see a way by which we could get right away under cover.

The only good cover, in that open, rather flat land, that I could see was an old overgrown cart track, with a high hedge both sides of it, that led from our spinney down to the village which the enemy had been searching. We heard their engines starting and watched two lorries proceeding out of the village in our direction. They were evidently going to search the farmhouse that we had just vacated. "We've got to get out of it," said Dike. "We'll just have to make a dash for it over the fields."

"Stay and fight 'em!" said Eli.

"We'll do neither," I said. And I led them into the green lane and straight down into the village that had just been searched. We found an empty house – an old vicarage I should imagine – with signs of recent searching, and made ourselves comfortable there. As I had guessed, the enemy did not come back to it. They were probably so unobservant that they did not even notice that we had been hiding in the farmhouse, and when they searched that they went away. This piece of low cunning earned me a lot of respect among my fellow bandits. Dike had been worried, I think, at the approach of the enemy, and even Eli realised that discretion was the better part of valour.

That night we all found ourselves bicycles. There were plenty of these about. Most country people had bicycles in their garden sheds, and wherever we went in East Anglia it was never difficult to find as many as we wanted. We mounted ourselves, and that night took the saddle and cycled first south-west and then south – and then struck east until we were in the woods of Sudbourne, well south of Gretford. There was a big stand of pine forest there, and we thought that we would be safer with plenty of trees around us. It was pretty obvious that in the open land we were vulnerable. In the forest we were safe.

And it was not long before we were having a drink in the Yeldham *Barge* again. And next day we blew up London Farming's main fuel-oil tank with a bazooka shell.

It would take too long to give a blow-by-blow account of a guerrilla campaign that went on, month after month, throughout the spring and well into the summer.

We never had any more targets as easy as the first three though.

The enemy began to guard things. They had not been attacked before. After the London Farming petrol tank, they withdrew most of the men that had been searching for us in the woods and about the countryside and put them on sentry-go. I am sure it was that which saved us. We were extremely mobile, and those great pine forests were ideal for moving unobserved in, and the enemy never knew where next we would strike. Thus, they had to put a guard on everything. Nor could they use a small guard – a mere half section of men. We might overwhelm anything less than a section. Any professional soldier knows how guard-providing uses up manpower. And he also knows how constant guard duty demoralises soldiers. I quickly saw that as long as we kept attacking, and kept mobile, and never stood for a battle, we would tie many of the enemy up on sentry-go and that they would find it hard to muster a sufficient force to drive the woods for us.

Although they began to guard everything static, such as dumps, barracks, officers' houses, petrol tanks, lorry parks and bridges, it was weeks before they learnt that it was dangerous for them to drive about the roads with lorries loaded with troops. The silly fellows seemed to think that safety lay in speed. We would lay up for them, generally at the bend of a road through the forest, where there was a nice clump of gorse or brambles on the strip between the rabbit netting that surrounded the pine forests and the edge of the road. We would probably be in two parties: one on the outside of the bend, the other fifty yards perhaps along the road. We would take great care to conceal ourselves, spending a long time doing this at night. By morning we would be ensconced. Then would come a long and terrible wait, with gorse prickles pricking us, flies and mosquitoes bothering us (at least as the summer came on), and the agony of lying for hours in one position. If any traffic came the wrong way we would lie still and let it go. Then – our game would come. A lorry loaded with troops, tearing along at high speed from the right direction.

When the lorry was just slowing down to take the corner, and about fifty yards from us – coming straight towards us – that is towards the party on the bend – we would fire at the driver with an automatic. We gave up the use of the bazooka for lorries to save ammunition. It was amazing how quickly the lorries used to swerve off the road and they would generally overturn. Then we would all open up – and the other party would open up too, from point-blank range often, depending upon where the lorry was. Dugdale's territorials had had big caches of grenades and mortar bombs and these we used freely. Few of the people who had been in the lorry used to escape. And long before any of their survivors had time to sort themselves out enough to fire back, the party down the road got out of it covered by the fire of the party on the bend and then the latter party would make its get-away. If we were quite sure they were all dead we would take the weapons and ammunition. We never left any wounded.

When I look back on those days I realise that, in spite of my fierce sorrow about my family, I had a kind of glory in the life. There were many times when we were cold, of course, or wet through for days and nights on end. There were times when we were terribly frightened. I lay under muddy water for two hours one night with my head just out and that covered with mud and water weed and under a bush. Soldiers were searching the bank of the fleet where I lay – like otter hounds drawing for an otter. I had been making the dangerous journey through the narrow neck of land between the Mudde and Gret. The crossing of the rivers themselves had become too dangerous, and this neck of land also was closely patrolled. We used to have to sneak through the woods of the narrow neck, at dead of night, and it was during one such transition that I was forced to hide thus uncomfortably in the water.

But the glory was in the excitement – in fellowship. I had never before felt so close to other men as I did then to our little band. Also there was the triumph when we pulled off a good coup, and the sheer animal joy that there is in living a life of freedom in the woods and fields.

We did not stick to the pine woods all the time. We found that the enemy's influence did not extend many miles from Willingham Castle. Most people hated the army, for the army had visited them all at one time or another, for one purpose only: to loot. People were friendly to us. Twenty miles away from Willingham we could be perfectly at our ease. We would lay up and rest. We would sleep in beds with interior-sprung mattresses, light fires in fireplaces – cook good meals. But we could never stay anywhere too long. The enemy were always after us and there was always the odd quisling – the odd informer.

A recruit or two trickled in. A surprising one was John Lloyd, the son of Sir Charles. He got to us through our Yeldham Ferry *Barge* grapevine. He was brought up to me in our current hide-out in the woods.

"My father sends his compliments, and says he would join you too if his rheumatism wasn't so bad," he said.

What's that you've got under your arm?" I asked.

"My father's elephant rifle," he said.

Another recruit was "Save-Soul" Jones.

It must not be supposed that we set ambushes time and again on the same road. I made myself unpopular with my little band by keeping them constantly on the move – they felt that I did this to excess. It made life uncomfortable for us of course. Whenever we had made ourselves a little bit comfortable in a forest camp, perhaps, with some rough pieces of canvas to keep out the rain, a store of food laid up, water handy, we would shoot up a lorry or a convoy, and then I would make them do an all-night forced march to put as many miles as possible between us and where we had been. Nor did we often use bicycles. These restrained us to the roads. The enemy were lords of the roads; we were masters off it. They seemed reluctant ever to leave their motor transport.

Then there was the terrible day we had our first casualty.

Eli had found that one man could stop a lorry as easily as the whole band, and we took to lying up in ambush in twos and threes. Eli, in fact, generally hunted by himself. He seemed to have an unquenchable thirst for it. But one day young Tom and I went off, and spent a horrible day lying among the new spring nettles under a clump of elder bushes. I did not quite like the place; we were on the road-side of the rabbit fence (that rabbit fence was always an embarrassment to us – we had to leap it before we would make our getaway) and the pine forest there was of the open type, with big trees and not much growing underneath them. We lay there for what seemed hours, and the cold November wind looked as if it would bring rain. I was beginning to hate rain. And as I lay there, beside Tom, turning sometimes on my back and sometimes on my tummy to relieve the cramp, I began to think thoughts of despair.

What was all this getting us to? Where could it lead? We were still only thirteen men by that time. Miraculously we hadn't lost one man, nor got one wounded, but only ten men had joined us since the start of our campaign. I had long ago given up all hope of seeing my family again. They were dead, although I could find no details of their deaths. The people in Gretford District were by no means unanimously on our side. The people I called true country people were, but our activities had made the army adopt such harsh measures with civilians that many people would have liked to see us hanged. Houses were constantly being searched, men taken off, people made to do more and more forced labour. (The fuel for the tractors really was short now: chiefly due to our efforts. We paid particular attention to the oil tanks and tankers.) Very little spring corn was got in that year, and all the potato planting was done by hand.

But there we were – we were not getting more popular. And there seemed to be no hope at all of us ever winning our war. We could kill a lot of enemy – no doubt – we had already killed a lot. But what good would it do us? There were thousands more. They would catch us sooner or later. One or two of my men were already talking about the advisability of our getting right out of it. Down in Essex perhaps – somewhere where the Midland army didn't go. Set up as privately-practising bandits on our own. I had been driving them terribly hard; I knew that I would not be able to keep their obedience for long. Anyway – what was the use? Revenge isn't really sweet; it is a bore. I felt that life had nothing more for me. I had come to a dead end. At least that is how I felt that day.

Then I heard the engine. At first I thought it was an aeroplane: one of those old-fashioned ones that had propellers. I hadn't seen an aeroplane since the CRASH. Even the army wouldn't squander England's last store of fuel to that extent. Then I realised that it was a vehicle, coming along the road. But slowly. Fear gripped my heart – there was something ominous about it. Then we saw it – an armoured car.

We had expected armoured cars before, but none had come. There had been rumours of them at Willingham, but they had been only rumours. And this thing was going slowly, and a man was standing in its turret scanning the road verges on both sides with field glasses. Behind came a lorry load of troops.

Our automatic rifle could do nothing against an armoured car.

It was moving slowly, and the officer in the turret was searching so carefully that we would certainly, in a few moments, be discovered. Then it was death. For a few seconds my judgement seemed to go away from me – I lay there and gaped. Then I said: "Scram Tom!" And I scrammed. I scrabbled out of my little tunnel under the elder bushes and took the rabbit fence at a bound, Tom with me. At the time I heard the rattle of machine guns from the armoured car. I got into the pines – and began to run as fast as I ever have, straight down one of the long, straight, horribly open lanes between the rows. I could hear Tom thumping behind me. My wits were back with me now. I realised that it would be a few moments before the armoured car, or the men in the lorry behind, had come up with the particular lane in which we ran. Until they did we might as well keep to the same lane – so as to make as much distance as we could. Before they did though we must leave the lane and start to go diagonally.

I heard more shots – the crack of bullets past my head. I dived through the row of pines to my left – then the next row – then the next – then ran fast down the lane I was in. Thank God there was a patch of high bracken in the forest – a place where, in years gone by, there had been a crag-pit, before Forestry Commissions were ever thought of. The men who dug that crag, to spread on their fields, saved my life. Just as more bullets cracked past my ears I dived into it. Through the bracken I went, out the other side, changed lanes, and went on, my heart thundering. I couldn't hear Tom. I stopped, panted, and listened. I was afraid my heart would give up. It thumped so that it was hurting me. I heard shouting – a whistle – more shouting. No Tom. I turned and ran on again, this time not so furiously: indeed if I had done I should have died of a heart attack as surely as if a bullet had hit me. I had no hope for Tom. I didn't even consider going back for him. I kept on running, walking, running, walking, until I could listen for a long time and hear nobody coming. Then, by a very circuitous route, I went through the forest until I got back to the gang.

They were where I had left them: camped in a patch of very

thick young pines, Corsicans that ought to have been thinned
long ago but had been missed. The gang had made small
clearings in there, thrown sacks and canvas over branches. It was
night by then and they had a small fire going. I remember vividly
coming up on them that night. I heard them before I got there,
for one of them was playing, very softly, on a mouth organ.
I whistled *The Larks*. There was silence – then the replying bar
came on the mouth organ.

And when I had forced my way through the prickly pine
needles and come into the clearing, there I saw my men's
unshaven faces, lit up from below the fire, and I saw their
blankets thrown over their shoulders, and for a moment my
misery and depression was lifted: there was something about the
fire-lit camp that fired something in me: plucked some string in
my breast that lifted my heart again.

"Tom's dead," I said. "Pretty certain." And I told them what
had happened.

"Give me that bazooka," said Eli. "That's what that armoured
car call for."

"It'd be suicide," said Cyril Blake.

"What!" said Eli. "I'm afraid of no armoured car."

"I think we ought to get the hell out of it," said Cyril. "We're
not getting anywhere like this. Let's get right out of the country.
We can still stick together. We'll do all right."

"What do you mean?" said Eli. "Not getting anywhere? We've
killed scores of the sods. And look at the damage we done 'em!"

"No-one come to help us," said Cyril's brother, Desmond.
"We'll just hang on in these woods and fight by ourselves until
we're dead. What's the good o' that? I want to live and enjoy
myself."

"You'll do what you're bloody well told!" said Eli. "You're in
this gang and you'll obey orders. The Cap'n's boss here!"

"Now then," I said. "Of course he'll obey orders but he won't
get silly orders, and he'll have a say in what the orders will be."

I realised that I was not the only one in the gang who was
beginning to feel the blank wall – the dead-end. I saw that we

must have a break. But I also knew that we must not appear to ourselves to be running away. We had suffered a defeat: we must have a victory before we left for a holiday and we must leave in our own good time.

"We will make a plan," I said. "Look here – that ambush today was on the Gretford-Willingham road. They must keep that road open at all costs – so that's where the armoured car will patrol most. We'll lay one good ambush for it – mine a bridge – that culvert at Butt Street. We'll take dam' good sure we can get away – that's the main thing. We'll fix that armoured car – then we'll clear out. We'll go to Essex, or somewhere, right away from the lot of them, and set up business there." And it was agreed. Next day we found Tom's body, shot through and through, and buried it under the pine needles.

We spent much careful planning on that next ambush.

We had fifty pounds of plastic High Explosive in our stores: what we used to call "808". Also a few electric detonators and a plunger. I sent for these (they were hidden somewhere down on the marshes) and, when they arrived, we laid the explosive under the culvert at the place called Butt Street: a ditch in the forest through which the road passed, but no street at all. We laid the cable, concealing it very carefully, to a point some thirty yards inside the perimeter rabbit-proof fence of the forest, and there placed the plunger. Dike was to use it. The forest in the dip was mixed: young beech and ash and silver birch. Good cover.

We placed the bazooka, with one man, in a hollow oak also about thirty yards in from the fence, but with a good command of the culvert. The rest of the gang took up a position on the other side of the plunger – on the Willingham side – ready to fire into any trucks that were following the armoured car and give the bazooka man time to do his job and then get away. Further – we found up a bicycle each and placed these bicycles handy behind us in the forest – at the point at which our good cover gave way to the endless straight rows of pine trees. We had found before that if you really pedalled like mad you could cycle for some distance over the pine needles. Our intention was to make for the leap on them and peddle as far as we could – then abandon them and run on foot. The man carrying the bazooka could not bike – but he was to get away before the rest of us, while we gave covering fire.

I was secretly sure that the armoured car would not turn up. I did not feel frightened, as we crouched in position that early morning: merely hopeless. If you wait up for a lion, I am told – it never comes. I was sure, after all that preparation, there would be no armoured car. I was wondering how we were going to break it to Eli that we were going for our long holiday, in safety, without avenging Tom's death. For I did not think our morale would stand much more without a rest.

And while I was thinking this – the armoured car came.

Again, very slowly, it came along the road. Just as we planned. Again the officer was scanning the verges. Everything depended now on our concealment, which after all, we had had to do in the dark. But the car was going a little faster than the time before, and the officer was perhaps not so careful. He had come a long way, from Willingham, and was perhaps losing his enthusiasm.

My heart was thumping as though I had been running! The car got nearer the culvert. And then it stopped!

They must have seen us. I wondered what the hell to do. Whether to open fire – and hope the bazooka would knock the car out. But I doubted if it was in good view of the bazooka. The man in the turret scanned around – I clearly saw his glasses looking straight at me for a moment. I knew I was well conceal- ed – my face blackened – my whole body covered with leaves – in thick cover. But if I could see him . . . ? The low morning sun was behind me – but not yet high enough to be shining in his eyes. I made up my mind to fire . . . then the car moved again. Forward. Slowly forward to within feet of the culvert – on to the culvert – starting to go over it . . . God! Dike must have forgotten to . . . BANG! It was John's elephant rifle. Then a tremendous explosion – a great tower of dirt and rubbish skyward – then a rain of bits of earth around our heads. And all hell let loose.

I had not seen the lorry behind the car, too scared to look I suppose. But there it was – and as the soldiers leapt over the side a hail of bullets came into them. Small mortar bombs began to burst among them. The bazooka roared – four times. Twice into the smitten car – twice at the lorry. I saw that the bazooka group then decamped. The rest of us went on firing – although there was by then no visible target – then I blew a whistle and we all got up and ran. We got to the bikes. I tried to ride mine – then gave it up and threw it away. The ground was too soft. I ran. We each kept in a different lane.

There was no pursuit. One reason might have been that we had arranged a number of booby traps between where we had lain and the road: grenades with instantaneous fuses in them instead of the usual five second ones – jammed in the forks of trees with their pins ready out and trip-wire rigged to pull them free. I heard some of these go off as I ran – but not until I had run an awful long way. I believe the first lorry-load was too shot up to follow anyway – it was men from a subsequent lorry who tried pursuit.

And we kept together, and had no casualties, and lost ourselves in forest, and we were none the worse.

I am convinced that determined guerrillas, in forest country, and – and this is the important thing – armed with automatic weapons with plenty of ammunition – will beat any regular troops. Automatic weapons give the ambusher such colossal hitting power – he can kill so many men in so few seconds – there is seldom any reply. The man lying in wait has enormous advantage over the men moving on the road.

But we were exhausted after the armoured car ambush. We had spent two days in preparation for it: walking miles and miles to fetch material, working all night to prepare our charge and hiding places – all we wanted was rest. We went as far as our current camping place and flaked out. And in doing so we ran into great peril.

Chapter Fourteen

by John Lloyd

Well my dear old Pater (Sir Charles Lloyd of Gretford) had this ancient double-barrelled elephant rifle – it was a Rigby four-fifty – and he had to have ammo specially made for it. He had a couple of hundred rounds and – I shouldn't boast, I know – but I was captain of the rifle-shooting team at Eton and I'd made two safaris in Kenya with old Pater and I can easily knock out a grant's gazelle running at three hundred yards and I thought well if I could get two hundred goes at the enemy I should certainly get a hundred of 'em.

Anyway – I might as well come out with it now but I was in love with Diana Hurlock. Everybody knew it anyway. Now both Pater and me (my mother's dead as you know) had got to hate this ruddy army. When that cad Brown bulldozed all the people's smallholdings my Dad nearly went mad. He stormed in and told Brown what he thought of him – mind you there never had been much love lost there, what? The man was an out-and-outer. Personally I hated the Midlanders. I didn't see what the hell they had to do coming to our neck of the woods. And then when I heard what had happened to Diana's family I simply saw red. It was bad enough when they harvested all Mr Hurlock's oats and worse still when they took him off to prison but when they took Diana and the rest of them too I really saw red. My father stormed over to *The Crown* and pulled that silly man Dobson out of the bar and created a hell of a scene. They actually arrested the old Dad and sent him to Willingham. I made up my mind there and then to do something about it. Then they let him go with a warning – the old Pater had been the squire of Gretford too long for them to do much to annoy him – he was pretty popular.

Then when I heard on the grapevine that Bob's whole family had been taken away to be shot; that was enough for me. My father was apoplectic. I really thought he was going to have a fit. As for me I was completely heart-broken, of course. All I could think of after I'd got over the shock was my father's elephant rifle. I lay in bed at nights just dreaming about what I was going to do with that elephant rifle. My father had several shotguns, of course – and I had a twenty bore and a four-ten – but I had to store my seven millimetre mauser with a friend in Kenya – I was only seventeen you see and they wouldn't give me a firearm permit in this country.

Anyway then there was this series of tremendous explosions in the night and in the morning we went out and saw the wreck of *The Crown*. The whole front was blown out of the building. A crowd had collected and there were soldiers keeping them back and I remember the look of elation on everybody's face. We were all delighted. Most of us, anyway.

Then of course it was war. We kept hearing more and more news of the guerrillas. I don't know how the news got out. The army never mentioned what was going on. The army suddenly got very hostile though. Most people had tolerated them at first – some people were bang on their side – but after the guerrillas started a tension grew up that you could cut with a knife.

A lot of retired people we had around Gretford supported the army. It represented "Law and Order" you see and they had oil. The real old country working chaps hated them. I think a lot of them could see that the oil wasn't going to last for ever, you know. And they hated the way Brown was farming the land. But the real thing was – the Midlanders were so bloody rude to them! The Midlanders were all city scum and they had no manners. They were always willing to suck up to my father because he was

a nob and all that, but they just couldn't find the time to be polite
to the country people. They had no manners.

So the moment I heard about the guerrillas I wanted to join
'em. I asked my father and the old man didn't say yes and he
didn't say no. He said wait awhile. I didn't feel I could leave old
Pater unless he let me. After all – he had nobody else except me
to look after him. But you see the army was behaving in a worse
and worse manner. To be fair the officers tried to stop it – and
they court-martialled quite a few bastards who were convicted of
rape etc. – and I believe they shot a few. But this didn't stop the
others. One night there was a particularly nasty event in the
house over the road – we won't go into it – and my father had
one of his apoplectic fits again. His face went red as a turkey –
and he stormed upstairs – came down with the elephant rifle and
made for the front door.

"Pater," I said. "Don't be a fool! What in blazes are you going
to do."

"Go to London Farming offices and shoot as many of these
brutes as I can before they shoot me!" Most of the troops were
billeted there.

I took the rifle away from him. I wrestled with him for it.
"Look Father!" I said. "Let me have the gun! I'm a damned good
shot. I'm better than you are. I'll go tonight and join the
guerrillas and I promise you for every two rounds of your ammo
I let off I'll kill one bastard!"

He sat down. He had to. I think he was very close to a heart
attack, or a stroke or something. I went and got a bottle of
whisky from the cellar. The old boy still had a few cases stashed
away. I poured out a stiff tot and he drank it.

Finally he recovered his breath. "All right," he said. "Go my
son. Live as long as you can. Don't take risks. Be a good
soldier." And all that. And, anyway, I left home that night and
took to the woods as you know.

I went to *The Barge* first, to find out where the boys were. I
had always been a habitué of the old *Barge*. I know I have a
Welsh name you know but my father's family had been in East

Suffolk for six generations that we knew of and everyone looked upon us as Suffolk people. My ma was a Cobbold. I had ever since a child liked the company of the real old Suffolk 'bors and they were my real friends. At Eton I was a bit of a misfit. I used to sail around to Yeldham in my fourteen footer and I was well-known there.

Well, to cut a long story short, I got shown to the hideout. I remember my heart leaping as I walked into that clearing in the middle of the forest. There were a few bits of green canvas tied over bushes – a fallow deer hung up in a tree – a small fire with a haunch of venison sizzling away on a spit over it – and all these bearded desperadoes! I remember bursting out laughing – I remember Wellington's remark about his mercenaries "I don't know what effect they'll have on the enemy but by God they terrify me!"

They made me welcome and laughed at the elephant gun. I thought there'd be some sort of swearing-in ceremony or something but all that happened was that Eli – who looked the fiercest devil you could imagine then and had a terrible wild look in his eyes – took me by the arm and said "You know what we're about? Well do you do what your a'told and you'll git on with we and we'll git on with you. The Cap'n's the boss and we does what he says."

That was all.

And three days later I was blooded, as you might say, at the armoured car ambush on the Willingham road. I fired both barrels at the officer standing up in the armoured car. I'm absolutely sure I hit him! Then I put another couple of rounds into the men jumping out of the truck. I know I hit several but in any case it was hard-nosed ammo and a bullet would go through several of them. I felt I was quite justified when we got back to the shelter in cutting two notches on the butt of my father's elephant rifle.

Well, after that we were in trouble!

We ate a huge meal that night – ate venison until it came out of our ears – then packed up and walked off through the forest north-west to where the Gret was fordable at low tide. Bob sent some scouts forward and they came back and whispered that there was a noisy group of soldiers over the other bank. That was one thing about Midlanders – they could never keep quiet.

Bob thought a bit and then sent four more scouts out – to probe other parts of the river where we might ford. They all came back, in a couple of hours, and said no go. It looked as if the whole river was guarded.

We retired further into the forest. Apparently the enemy had not bothered guarding the river before – only the bridges and the short neck of land between the two rivers.

"Let's try the Mudde," said someone. We heard some lorries going along the forest lane that runs from Sibford to Bebbage – on our side of the river.

I could see the tension in the faces of my companions. I knew that we were in extreme danger. Bob decided to withdraw to a safer place deeper in the forest.

When we got to this thick cover he stationed sentries on each side and sent six scouts out: two brothers, Cyril and Des Blake, southward to the Mudde and the other four east to the River Gret higher up than we had been before. We could hear the sound of lorry engines from all sides. We all had the same fear. We were being surrounded.

All that long night we lay to our arms. I think you know that was no ordinary bunch of chaps. I think every man would have died right there rather than give in. I remember hearing old Eli say: "I don't mind a'dyin' but I in't killed enough on 'em yet!"

I'll never forget that dreadful night in the forest! Just lying there, in the wet pine needles – it was raining which didn't help to cheer us up – waiting for those scouts to come back with their reports and wondering what the hell we were going to do. And every now and then hearing lorry engines revving up in the distance.

The day came. We didn't dare light a fire. Two of the scouts came back from the Gret – then the other two. They both reported: no-go. Troops – everywhere. One of them had seen armoured troop carriers going by. We hung on and waited for the Blake brothers.

"Why don't one of us go to *The Barge*?" asked Dike. "That'll be open now."

"There'll be soldiers there," said Bob.

"Look!" I said. "I'll go. Nobody knows I've been with you. I'll go and hide my gun and simply walk in. I'm not under suspicion. Look – I can go home, have a bath and change of clothes, even shave off this stubble of mine!"

They laughed at this but in the end Bob decided to let me go. "If there's soldiers there just come back and tell us," he said. "Go in and have a drink and hear what you can and come back and tell us. If there's no soldiers find out whatever you can about the enemy."

So off I went, with my elephant rifle and a belt of ammo, and near Yeldham Ferry I hid the gun and the ammo. I then walked on to Gretford. Old Pater wasn't in the house as I changed and cleaned myself up. Then I walked back through the woods to Yeldham Ferry. When I got there I walked out of the woods as bold as brass but feeling my knees shaking. Into the pub I went.

There were no soldiers but half a dozen chaps. Most of them were relations of the men I had been in the forest with and they were all my friends. I asked them what they knew. The country's filling up with soldiers they said. Outside the windows I could see two high-sided grain lorries. London Farming had an outlying grain silo just behind *The Barge* and here were these two grain lorries come to carry grain away. I had an idea. I feel a bit shy about telling all this – I didn't do what I did because I was any sort of hero – I was scared stiff. But it seemed the only thing I could possibly do.

"How many people in those grain lorries?" I asked.

"Two. Two drivers. Both soldiers."

I could see them out of the window. They were leaning together against a rail, talking to a London Farming man.

I spoke to Harry Blendover. I told him – and the others there – what the position was. "I want one of those grain trucks," I said.

"Wait here. Don't say a thing. Don't give me away or stop me doing what I'm going to do."

I ran out to where I'd left the elephant rifle. I jammed two rounds into the breech of what was a double barrel you know – and walked quietly to the edge of the wood. I aimed – fired – a right and a left. "I've got 'em," I shouted. I ran towards the lorries. The London Farming man had disappeared – round the corner somewhere.

The soldiers were both dead.

They had army forage hats on – with badges of the Mercian Regiment on them. I grabbed the hats – flung them in one of the lorry cabs – and hauled myself up into the high cab. I fumbled about trying to start the engine. I could drive all right – had often driven Pater's old Rover – and I'd driven tractors on Bob's farm but I couldn't start this damned thing. Suddenly my heart nearly jumped out of my mouth as the door opened and someone jumped in. It was Harry Blendover! "Get you on over the other side!" he said. He got into the driving seat and started the engine. "You tell me where to go," he said.

"Put the dam' hat on!" I told him. I did the same. We drove along the main forest road and passed an armoured troop carrier on the way! We waved at them – they waved back. We drove straight down the ride toward where the gang were hidden. I was scared stiff they'd fire at us. Thank God I recognised a big oak that had been left by the Forestry and I remembered that our first sentry was a hundred yards or so further on. We stopped and I jumped out. I ran forward. I was feeling a sense of panic now. I cupped my hands and shouted: "It's me! It's all right – it's me! John Lloyd! Don't shoot! It's me!"

"Shut you up – you'll wake the whole dam' forest!" said a voice. It was Eli.

I told him what I'd done. "Run you on and tell the Cap'n," he said. "I'll go and get the lorry."

I ran back – Bob mustered all the men who were there – we heard the lorry coming and there was a space there in the pine trees just enough to turn her. Turn here we did.

Now, several of the men wore army greatcoats that they had kept from the territorial days. We decided that two of us should sit in front, wearing army greatcoats and the forage hats. The rest should clamber in the back where the wheat was to go.

Bob and I shook hands with old Harry Blendover and left him standing there in the forest. That was the last time any of us saw him. Suddenly someone remembered the Blake brothers.

"Cyril and Des ain't back!" said someone.

"They'll have to take their chance," said Bob. "If we wait for them we'll all die. If we go now we'll have a chance."

Dougie Burrows was a long distance lorry driver and the only one of these bandits who was clean-shaven so it was agreed that he should drive. I got up beside him. The rest all crawled in the back. It must have been like a huge great empty tank in there and they couldn't see a thing.

Dougie drove like hell. We came out onto the road and saw no-one but then on the main forest road we began to pass troops. At one place we saw about forty men spreading out along the edge of the forest and advancing into it – one man to a space between two rows of trees. They didn't even look at us. Our truck had a big army insignia on it anyway. We soon learned to ignore soldiers.

We turned right onto the main road near *The Barge* and thundered off along the road towards Gretford. There were troops everywhere. At Chillingham we turned right and made for the Randersfield road. At the narrow bit between the Gret and the Mudde we knew we would come to a big road block. We did – there was a barrier across the road and all. I believe they had surrounded the whole area between the two rivers with a ring of men. We had to wait while a whole convoy of lorries, all carrying troops, filed through the road block. The military policeman waved us on. But as we drew near him he held up his hand. My heart sank right through my boots. He strolled up to the driver's side. Thank God it was not my side I thought. I could never have faced him.

"Where are you going?" he said, in his Birmingham accent.

"Brum," said Dougie as cool as a cucumber. "With wheat".

"Wish I was going with you ," said the redcap and waved us on.

We by-passed Randersfield and held on towards Willingham. We decided it was better to drive through it than to by-pass it although we knew it was full of troops. Actually when we got to it we found it almost deserted – presumably every man-jack had been dragged out looking for us.

The other side of Stowmarket, on the A45, we nearly had another heart attack. There was this staff car, heading the way we were, but broken down. Four men stood beside it, three of them officers. One of them walked into the road and held his hand up.

"Drive on!" I said.

But to my horror Dougie started to pull up. "They'd only catch us if we did," he said.

He stopped. The officer said: "Where are you going?"

"Brum, with wheat," I answered. And then remembered to say "Sir!"

"Are you going through Cambridge?"

Dougie leant over me. "Yes, we are Sir!" he said. This worried me because I knew that was not the intention at all.

"Well you will take this officer with you," said the man. "Bill – come on – here's a lift to HQ."

In got officer Bill, Doug drove off, and Bill started to ask us lots of awkward questions. What lot were we in? Who was our officer? etc. etc. Dougie just drives along the road answering in grunts. The officer was trying to be friendly. Telling us about himself, quite a nice chap too.

"What – the Third Transport? Never heard of that? What do you mean?" he says in response to an answer we gave.

"Look," says Dougie and begins to slow down. "Excuse me, Sir, but I'm bursting for a pee. Another thing – I'm a bit worried about one of the back wheels. It's got a very slow puncture."

He stopped – and got out.

At first I thought Bill was not going to follow him but then, thank God, he did. He evidently wanted to pee too. Probably hadn't wanted to in front of his superior officer.

Bill walked round the front of the lorry and stood relieving his nature in the hedge. Dougie jumped back into the cab and drove off. We could hear shouts of "Stop!" Dougie did stop.

"Use your elephant gun," he said.

I got out, leant my left hand on the mirror bracket for support, aimed and squeezed. Bill looked as though he'd been hit by a thunderbolt. I climbed back and, as we thundered along the road carved three more notches – two for the two drivers at *The Barge* and one for Bill. I felt a bit sad for Bill. He seemed a nice chap really. He told us he'd been at one of the minor public schools.

At Woolpit we turned right and headed for Thetford. We were aiming for the Breckland forests for that's where Bob had decided we should go. Those forests were vast – the second biggest forest in England.

Thetford seemed full of troops. We saw tanks there. We kept along the A134 and turned off the road to the left and drove to a place called Grimes Graves. This interested me because the Pater had taken me there once. There were old Palaeolithic flint mines there. Dougie stopped the truck and a hoard of thoroughly stiff and fed-up bandits crawled out the back of it.

"Goo to hell thass wuss than the duzzy tomb in there!" said one of them.

"Doug," said Bob. "Take the lorry back to the main road, drive it back towards Thetford about a mile, and dump it, preferably over a bank."

"Hadn't we better keep it, Skip?" said Dougie. "Happen we might want to go for another joyride."

"No," said Bob. "Dump it." And that was that.

We waited until Dougie came back. He'd let the lorry run over an embankment – got out first himself, of course. We then wandered into the forest.

Fortunately the one thing Bob had was maps. He had the complete set of East Anglia. He spotted where there was a forest hut and we found it. It was empty and deserted.

We broke the padlock on the door – and went in – and I think it was then we realised how exhausted we all were. We all had our blankets slung over our shoulders. This was our uniform really. We'd roll our blanket up into a tight roll, rolling any spare food and a tin cup and a few odds and ends in it – then hang the roll over our left shoulder and tie the two ends together on our right hip. Surprising how comfortable that was, and it gave us freedom to use our rifles.

Well we flung down the blankets, some of us gobbled up some cold venison, we drank from a stream outside the door, and then flung ourselves on our blankets and went to sleep. Bob detailed sentries but I had a peculiar feeling that none of us were going to take our duties very seriously that night.

Chapter Fifteen

by Bob Hurlock

After that nightmare journey in the grain truck – and thank God and young John we had it – I awoke to find the sun shining in the open doorway of the hut. The place seemed full of people. People standing up. Men with automatic rifles in their hands. Pointing them at us.

I sat up and grabbed for my gun.

"Steady!" said a man standing over me pointing a gun at me. "Steady now. Don't shoot and you'll be all right."

I dropped my gun. "Who are you?" I said.

"Who are you?"

I could see they were not soldiers. They all had beards, like we did. They all wore different clothes. Dyed green though.

"There's a lot more of us outside but if you keep quiet we shan't hurt you," said the man. Others of my men began to wake up. I got to my feet. "Don't shoot anybody!" I said. "These are friends."

I had no idea whether they were friends or not but I desperately didn't want my men to shoot. You never knew what Eli would do. And we were covered and outnumbered.

"Where the hell's my bloody sentry?" I asked.

"Sleeping like a little child," came this strong Lincolnshire voice. "You'd ha looked funny if we'd bin the Midlanders."

By this time my companions had all woken up – I still had to restrain them from reaching for the triggers.

We all got up, looking sheepish (why is it one always feels sheepish when discovered asleep in daylight?) and introduced ourselves to the strangers. I saw there were more outside: perhaps twenty. All dressed in green. I was reminded of Robin Hood. I was certain they were not army.

"Where are you from?" said their leader.

"Suffolk. The coast." I wasn't going to give anything away.

"Are you running away from the Midland army?" he said.

"We're not running away from anybody," I said. "We're just living as best we can, independently, and harming nobody. We're not bandits."

"You carry all that hardware about to shoot rabbits?"

"No – er – to defend ourselves if necessary."

"You might as well come out with it – you didn't come all this way without running into the army. They're all over East Suffolk."

"Go on then – tell us what you are."

"All right mate. My name's Jim Holden. I'm in command of the seventh squad of Fen Tigers. We're Lincolnshire Fenmen; yellowbellies; red-earth Fens. And we have declared war against the men who wouldn't let us have the wherewithal to save our Fens."

I shook hands with him. I told him who we were.

"I've heard all about you," he said. We've got several deserters from the army in our lot. How many of you chaps is there?"

"Ten. There were thirteen."

"Good God – the army put you at a hundred or more!"

It was delightful – a great relief – to find that we were not alone in our fight. It made the whole thing seem more sense – more hopeful. Our hearts leapt up – we felt our war was won.

"Are there many of you?" asked Dike.

"We've got eleven squads now I think it is – of roughly twenty men a piece. We could get ten times the number. No weapons. Weapons and ammo – that is our problem."

"Can we join you?" I asked.

"I reckon so – it's a matter for the Chief, chap named Jenkins.

Hereward the Wake, we call him. I know what he'll say though."

"What?"

"Stick it out in your own country. You'll do far more good there. There's enough of us here to keep 'em busy."

I saw the sense of this. I also saw that now we knew that we had friends in the world – we would be able to stick it out in our own country. We would have more stomach for the fight. It didn't seem hopeless any more. And Jim Holden told us that there were other bands of guerrillas: in the forest north of Nottingham, in the Lincolnshire Wolds and in the Trent Valley.

Word was sent to Jim Jenkins, the leader of the Fen Tigers, that we were there. He invited us to a feast. We were taken to the temporary headquarters: deep in the forest, south of Brandon. Jenkins was there with a staff of about twenty men: all clad in green dyed clothes. Jenkins himself was an enormous, red-bearded, extrovert of a fellow, all bluster and bombast. One could imagine him before the CRASH, being just a misfit, but now he came into his own. He had been an amateur actor in his time, and he acted now: very well too. He was probably the only man who could have held his job, for his problem was to keep the peace among the Norfolkmen and the Lincolnshiremen in his command. Not that they would have been at each others' throats: simply that the Norfolkmen wanted a Norfolkman to command them; the Lincolnshiremen one of their own people. In the Fens there is a great gulf fixed. The crossing of the parish boundary would take you from broad Norfolk into broad Lincolnshire – and a people who are far more like Yorkshiremen than they are like their East Anglian neighbours: temperament, values, outlook on life are all different. Regional differences that had seemed dead before the CRASH were all to be seen again.

But here was this man Jenkins – born and brought up in King's Lynn but, having practised for years as a doctor near Boston, he could talk both languages.

He was sitting at a table under a lorry-tilt thrown over some poles. He was looking at maps – no poring over them would be the better expression. I had the feeling that he had started "poring" when our arrival was announced. He strode out – head and shoulders above his men – red beard waving – came towards me and boomed:

"Gretford!"

"Doctor Jenkins I presume," I murmured.

"Wine!" he bellowed. "Wine."

Wine was brought – by a very pretty girl. The doctor lived well.

"We've heard all about you," the doctor said, as we all sat down in the clearing, on boxes and logs of wood, and took wine in our hands. "The scourge of Suffolk. But we always thought you had an army of several hundred."

"We've never heard of you," I said. "We never get any news our way."

"We've had prisoners. We have ways and means of making them talk. We've got deserters too. They talk, all too much. We get our news from the enemy. We know what happens north, south, east and west. (Fill Gretford's glass, Joan)."

The succulent smell of a deer being roasted on a spit nearby came to our nostrils.

"Before we get too drunk," said the doctor, "come over here."

Dike, Eli and I went over to the table under the canvas tilt, on which lay the map.

Jenkins made a dramatic sweep with his hand. "Brecklands," he boomed. "And here – Fens. Flooded now. But islands – plenty of islands still. It's as it was in Hereward the Wake's day."

"Is there deep water where the islands aren't?" I said.

"No. That's a fallacy. Lots of swamp – marsh – places flooded at high spring tides or when it rains hard – soft mud at other times. Some flooded permanently of course. But we still move about in the Fens. They're our retreat. When the enemy press us too hard here in the forest, we say goodbye and shoot down to the Fens. That's the job. Keep hitting them here until they get fed up with it and bring in a big army from the Midlands. Then we disappear. Stay away until they're gone – or hit them over the other side. Wait until they've withdrawn their main forces and then come back here again."

"Haven't they tried to follow you into the Fens?"

"Haven't they indeed! They have! They won't any more though."

"Didn't pay 'em?"

"No. They did the paying. They're road-bound. There are no roads left in the Fens. We've blown the bridges. They tried the rivers. You've got to be a good man to use our rivers. Seven knot tides – what? They've tried marching. We blew a wall once – drowned a hundred. They keep their noses out now."

"How do you feed so many men?"

"Feed them? We're Fenmen aren't we? Finest farmers in the world. Before the bomb we fed half England. Now we've only got an eighth of the land left perhaps – just the high ground – but on that we can grow more than we'll ever eat. And our women – we've somewhere to leave 'em. A firm safe base. Somewhere to fall back on."

"I wish we had," said Dike. "All we've got to fall back on's the sea, and that's not much good to us. We can only take bachelors in this lot."

"One thing you seem to have that we haven't got," said Jenkins. "And that's arms, and ammo. We're very short – we can't take more men in. Can't even give 'em rifles. We depend on what we can loot from the army nowadays. Look here," and another grand sweep of the doctor's hand.

"See that road? Huntingdon – Cambridge – Newmarket – Thetford." He thumped his fingers down on each place named. "That's the enemy's only way to your country. That's our target. That road. That's one of their main lines of communication. We have ambushes along it nearly all the time. Now if you chaps can give them as much trouble as you can in Suffolk they'll be forced to use that road more and more. They must. Send troops along it – oil. And we'll hit 'em as they go. Don't you worry. They pay toll on that turnpike."

We sat down to an enormous meal of venison and bread. There

were some thirty people at the feast. Two men who came in late were Tony Larkin, and Michael Self: the two men whom I had become most friendly with in the prison camp at Wretham.

"So you escaped then?" I said to them.

"Yes – soon after you did. We had a mass break-out. They've closed that camp. Too many men escaped into the forest. Half the chaps here were in there. They removed the rest to Nottinghamshire – they work in the coal mines there, I believe."

"Hullo!" roared Jenkins to me across the fire. "You've found our official philosopher! We carry on the war. Larkin there tells us why we carry it on!"

"And why do we?" I asked Larkin.

"The Marxist interpretation," said Larkin, "and Marx would have been right, although he was wrong some times, would be that this war is a struggle between two interests – two cultures – economies – and ways of life. To put it very simply it is a struggle between the oil-users – the city-centred people – and the peasants. We are the peasants. As long as the city people have oil – they will be unbeatable. We will harry them from the woods – that is all we can do. If their oil dries up – they will wither away. They are quite helpless without it. Oil gives them power. The bulk of the country people will be on their side as long as they can give them oil for their tractors. The country people will take anything – put up with anything – from the army as long as it will give them oil. If they had given us oil to run our Fenland pumps we would not be here now. If oil started coming in from outside the country our case would be hopeless. If it doesn't come – we will win."

"What puzzles me," said Dike, "is how much oil the beggars seem to have. I should have thought that's a' been finished months ago."

Michael Self said: "The government had stored huge stocks, fearing a war. They knew the country might be cut off. I think the army has discovered supplies that they didn't know existed at first. And after all – there were twenty million cars on the roads – now there are a few hundred. I don't myself think we can hope

for the oil to dry up for a few years. I don't agree with Tony.
I think we've got to beat 'em – by force of arms. And then
replace a bad government by a good one. That's all. Nothing
about Marxism – or oil."

"Beat 'em!" roared Jenkins. "Of course we can beat 'em – oil
or no oil. Come on – that's enough about oil and all that squit!
Oil your throttles with some good looted wine – and give us a
song or two!"

There was a fearful man with a piano accordion. They didn't
seem to mind how much noise they made. "We know where the
enemy are," said Jenkins. "And where they aren't. And they
aren't near here. Let's have a song!"

If the enemy had happened on us that day we would have been
easy meat. We all got hopelessly and monumentally drunk.

We stayed in the Brecklands a week, being feasted by Jenkins
and his green-clad merry men, and a great diversion it was too.
Then we mounted bicycles and rode through a couple of nights
until we came to our own country again. We had had news that
the bulk of the enemy's force had gone back to the Midlands
from the Willingham area. They had given up searching for us in
East Suffolk. We crossed the Gret, dug up our bazooka from
where it had been buried in a badger's earth, and went and blew
up the London Farming offices – just to let people know we were
back.

And after that we fought with renewed vigour, because we
knew we were not alone. And we fought with more effect. And
people began to join us. We built up an elaborate secret
recruiting system.

While we had been away the army had weighed very heavily on
the countryside. In their search for us, and for arms, time and
time again, they had taken people away, shot people, looted,
raped.

Most of the soldiers were just ordinary men, although some
had been the scum of the earth to start off with; but all of them
had for months been living by looting. They were rootless now
and in what seemed to them like a foreign country. They behaved

as troops do behave in foreign countries – particularly countries
which they have conquered. And so recruits came to join us. We
soon had thirty men. With this force we raided the prison up near
Lowestoft: an old civil jail in which they kept any person they
wanted to lock up. We broke it open and released two hundred
people. Fifty of those we enrolled and armed.

Then we began to take the initiative – out of the forests as well
as in them. We ceased to be just fugitives with a kick in them.
We began to mount big offensives. We attacked the guards of
bridges and blew the bridges up. We served both the two bridges
over the Mudde and Gret like this. We made all movement by
vehicles along the roads impossible. One section dropped twenty
four-inch mortar bombs behind the wall of Willingham Castle.
True they never came back to tell the tale, but we heard that the
damage they did was terrific.

For months – right through the winter and into summer – we
hammered and hammered at the enemy.

Ammunition became very tight: until we had word from an
army deserter of the imminent arrival of an ammunition convoy
from the Midlands. We mustered every man we had and made a
full-scale attack. We were lucky. We had no more care about
ammunition.

Civilians helped us more and more. Many of our helpers were
young boys and girls and they operated most effectively often
without leaving their villages. Sugar in army petrol tanks.
Slashed tyres. Cut telephone wires, information as to where
officers were billeted. It all helped. A sack of sugar chucked
down the thousand-gallon petrol tank at the Gretford garage
helped most of all perhaps.

We were not universally popular, of course. The army was
punishing the countryside severely and many people blamed it on
us. "If it wasn't for those bandits – the army would leave us
alone!"

But it was for the bandits. And men and women of spirit came
and joined us. In fact when we got back from the Brecklands it
was to find a small gang operating: led by the brothers Cyril and

Des Blake. After we had left the district, during the big drive against us, these two men had been left behind; had missed us, and had been driven about in the forest like hunted rabbits for a week. Soldiers had driven the woods with one man to each lane between the trees – so nothing could be missed. The brothers hid every day for three days in the branches of a huge oak tree in an oak wood, coming down by night for water and rest. The soldiers had passed underneath them three times, but had not seen them up in the branches.

Deserters from the army began to come to us. Many of them left the army because they did not like the atrocities that some of their officers committed, or ordered to be committed. For as the enemy became more on the defensive, more harassed, so they became more ruthless. But it was not until September, when the enemy collected one man from every parish around Gretford, brought them into Gretford Square, lined them up against the wall and shot them, then the trickle of recruits to us became a flood.

It was soon after then that word reached us that the army was willing to discuss terms.

A letter came to us. We sent a reply.

By devious means a meeting was arranged. Three army officers would meet one of our men at an arranged place in the forest. They would then be led to our temporary headquarters.

The three officers arrived. A volunteer (John Lloyd in fact) met them (he was being covered by a dozen hidden automatics) and he led them far into the forest, some of our men forming a screen behind them to make sure they were not being followed. They came into the clearing in which a dozen other chaps and I were waiting for them. There was a major and two captains. We all sat down on logs.

"I am instructed to say," said the Major, "that the army will leave the area bounded by the Mudde and the Gret if you cease to attack us."

"First you must return all the people that you have taken away from this district," I said.

"Some of them are in the Midlands. It would take a month to organise."

"Organise it then." I suddenly had a mad, wild hope that Jessie and the kids might be among them.

"And meanwhile – a cease-fire?"

"From the moment when the last of your men crosses the rivers."

"I think that – I can provisionally accept that on behalf of my colonel," he said.

"Good," I said. "Now that's over perhaps we can have a drink!" And somebody produced a bottle of Mother Denny's terrible home-made wine.

They proved quite ordinary chaps and became quite friendly. The major had been an insurance clerk in Nottingham. The other two had both been salesmen. They said that they had disapproved of a lot of what their army had done – but what could they do? If anyone protested, and a few people had, they had soon been whipped off to some local equivalent of Siberia.

"Can you tell me," I asked them, "what's happened to one of your chaps – a Captain Hugh Giles?"

"Giles," said the Major. "He blacked his copy-book. Skipped – with some other disaffected chaps. We're always getting desertions you know. But it takes a lot to desert – when you know which side your bread's buttered on."

"No doubt it does," I said.

They were taken away, and the next day, according to plan, the army began to move over the Gret. They had to walk – no transport – no bridges. They left a lot behind them. All their heavy stores. They seemed quite demoralised. Cautiously, my guerrillas moved into Gretford. We found quarters there, in the many empty houses. We set about the task of restoring the shattered countryside.

After a fortnight a batch of forty people arrived, from the Brecklands. There were men, women and children – but no Jessie – none of my children – nor was Mary, Eli's wife there.

Our war was over, at least for the time.

Chapter Sixteen

by Lieutenant-Colonel John Nightingale

(. . . continuing his account of events.)

Well; by the middle of February *20 - -*, in spite of the continuing extreme arctic weather, I began to feel that I was getting much better in control of the little isolated kingdom of which I found myself reluctant king, and I felt that there was perhaps a glimpse of a rainbow in the darkening sky.

The fact that millions of people had already died relieved the pressure enormously. It began to make sense to send lorries into the country and requisition food and start rationing people. It began to make sense to send for coal, of which there were huge dumps by various abandoned power stations. I set my men on to organising the burial of the thousands of deep-frozen bodies that lay about all over the city, in building excavations. We got the water supplies going again. We even got electricity happening in key buildings such, I may say, as my own headquarters.

We soldiers were comfortable enough. After all – it would have been to nobody's benefit for us to have neglected ourselves. I believed that the only hope for the restoration of civilisation lay in the army. I was going to keep the army alive and well, and in control, no matter what happened at all.

I began to try to help the farmers, because I realised that without their efforts we would all eventually starve.

I started a system of billeting a few men on each farm. These men were to keep order among the people who tended to crowd in to where there was some food and shelter, to encourage many of these people to go back to the cities where we could feed them, and to make the ones that stayed work. We had found large stores of petrol and oil by then but still did not feel that we had enough to issue too much out to the farmers. I wanted to keep a good reserve for army use. So the farmers were forced to use more and more hand labour.

I believe this movement stopped after the initial pouring out into the countryside by starving millions. It was better to keep the people in the cities and bring the food to them. In the country they formed unruly gangs and even killed farmers, and we knew it was only the farmers who could feed us all. So I ordered patrols to shoot anyone they found wandering about with a gun. Up with that I would not put.

My patrols pushed further and further out into the country away from Birmingham. They began to make contacts with other military commands. At first these military commands seemed pretty well autonomous. There was no friction between us but there was no high command. Around Shrewsbury there was a battalion of the Shropshire Light Infantry; Stoke-on-Trent had the Staffordshire Yeomanry; Coventry, Nottingham and Leicester were looked after by the Sherwood Foresters; and we had various units to the south-east, south and south-west. It all worked quite amicably. No soldiers ever fired on each other.

Then, one day, who should arrive in Birmingham, driven in a staff car and with an escort of armoured cars, but the Commander-in-Chief of the British Army.

I came back from a tour of the Warwickshire area and walked into my office to be told by my secretary: "General Sir Charles Wicklow to see you, Sir!"

And there was that great man, as large as life, sitting in an armchair beside my booze cupboard.

He got up, shook hands, and said: "Afternoon, Nightingale." I had the worst of forebodings. I did not like the man, although I had been at Sandhurst with him.

"We're going to have an all-army conference," he said. "Here, in Birmingham. It's central. You will organise it."

"How are things in the South?" I asked.

"Better. Most of London died. Place is a ghost city. Uncontrollable. We did our best – tried to control it – nothing we could do. They died by millions. God knows what will happen when the warm weather comes. We haven't been able to get in to bury 'em. Decided to leave 'em alone. Thousands got out though. It's those we've got to worry about. Keep 'em alive."

"What do you want to do now?"

"Take command. Get the army together again – under one command. Whole thing will fall to pieces if we don't."

"What about the North?" For I knew there was another general up there who had been going about saying that he was the ruler of England.

"Beverley? He's junior to me. Sorry. He'll have to do what he's told."

"What about Wales?"

"They've declared UDI. Like the Rhodesians did. It didn't help them, did it. Won't help the Taffs. As soon as we can we'll have to bring 'em to book."

Well, to cut a long story short, dispatches were sent out to the officers commanding all the units of the Midlands and southern England; and we had the conference; it lasted three days and an awful lot of whisky was drunk; and then the High Command gave its orders.

I was ordered immediately to take over East Anglia. I was to be centred at Cambridge. I was pleased about this because, I reflected, that the colleges would make good billets. I also had a few thoughts about the college wine cellars. My orders were to take over the government of the whole area, keep order, encourage the farmers to grow food, try to get industries going again.

"What's happened to the civilian government?" I asked Wicklow. "Can't have disappeared into thin air."

"Well it has. Sunk without trace. The King's alive. He went to

Balmoral. Lives on grouse I suppose. He's all right. Parliament's deserted. Finished. Civil servants – all the pen-pushers – starved to death. Big fires there were in London. People started burning all the woodwork to keep warm – and the thing got out of hand. No water in the hydrants to put 'em out. People swarmed out into the countryside – we shot hundreds of 'em – orders to keep 'em in. Couldn't though. They overwhelmed all the home counties. Absolutely ruined everything. Like locusts they were. But it didn't do 'em any good. Then the country people began to rally, and get the territorials going, and they put up road blocks, and blew up bridges, and simply stopped the Londoners going any further. Millions starved to death. If they stayed in town they could keep warm but they starved – and no water. If they went into the country they froze in the snow. Terrible. There was nothing we could do."

So accordingly, I called in all my units – rallied them at Leamington – and we set off in a large convoy for East Anglia, my new command.

We were quite a big army by then. By recruiting we had trebled the size of the battalion: we were more like a brigade. I decided to organise it on brigade lines. I couldn't promote myself to Brigadier of course – that would have to come through from Second Echelon and the Lord knew what had happened to that.

Well, Cambridge was just as I thought it would be. Just what we wanted for a headquarters. We even found some wine left in some of the college cellars. The cellars of Peterhouse, I remember, were very kind to us. I and my staff took over Kings.

I allotted areas to my new battalion commanders (my former company commanders really) but ordered them to behave with some circumspection. They were to find their headquarters and then slowly push their patrols out, as tactfully as possible, into the countryside, with no friction with civilians if they could avoid it, and eventually, but slowly, take over the whole area. The last thing I wanted was a fight.

But I realised quite early on that there would be friction. After all, my Mercians (we were a fairly new regiment – formed in the reshuffle of 1985) were all city men. They didn't seem too tactful with the country people. The "yokels" they called them. Or "swede-bashers" and other such endearments. Not a happy scene at all.

The First Battalion, as I called my jumped-up A Company, that features most in the story of this book, had its headquarters in Bury St. Edmunds. They met with little trouble or resistance in West Suffolk. The farms were huge, like Cambridgeshire, big company farms. The managers and bailiffs co-operated and we had no trouble from them at all. It was only when they got into East Suffolk that they began to smell trouble. But it was some time before they got as far as that.

From time to time we met with territorials. These had been mobilised at the CRASH to control things and try to keep the city people from swarming over too much territory. Where we could we simply took these over, and re-enrolled the men in the regular army.

Policy was laid down from High Command on this. We were not to suffer independent units of territorials to exist. They were either to be enrolled – or disarmed and sent home. If they were enrolled then they were to be transferred to other units far from their homes.

That is why my Mercians were sent to East Anglia. The policy was not to keep soldiers near their homes. The powers that were could see that this might lead to trouble.

You see, the territorials were for the most part countrymen. They could not be expected to help in the requisitioning of food to be taken to the cities. They were known in fact, on occasions, to oppose such requisitioning. Now this simply would not do.

I had every sympathy with the farmers. After all – they grew the food. They were the only people in the country who really mattered. But they were a tiny minority. The vast majority of the people of England were city people. True, millions of these had died but millions still survived. My policy – and the policy of High Command – was to leave the farmers themselves just enough food to live on and requisition the rest for the cities.

We started trying to set up a civil service again. Food rationing was introduced. Farmers were forbidden to hoard food. We had to take pretty draconian measures about this. I had the unpleasant duty, enjoined on me by High Command, to establish big work camps in the Breckland Forests. No doubt my old enemy and present friend Bob will tell us a lot about these. At first several farmers, and other people found hoarding, got sent to these. Then I gave orders to be far more lenient with farmers – to turn a blind eye in fact. You see it was becoming more and more obvious that we needed the farmers free. I think we city people had always taken farmers for granted before.

At first the farmers were not too reluctant to let us take their food for we gave them oil in exchange. None of them were geared up for hand labour, although that was the one thing that was in plentiful supply. City people were only too delighted to get a billet on a farm, and work in return for warmth and food. But the farmers simply couldn't handle their labour. There were not enough hand tools for example. Supervision was impossible and the city people were quite extraordinarily inept. I had several meetings with groups of farmers in my area and began to understand the problems that they would be facing. Weeds, for example. For many decades weeds had been controlled by poisonous chemicals. These chemicals would no longer be forthcoming. The hoe would have to take their place; farmers, when the summer came, would have to start hoeing again. But the mind boggled at having to hoe a thousand-acre farm. It took a man, I was told, a week to hoe an acre, and then he had to be a good man and used to the job. Ploughing, getting a seed bed, and drilling would be possible, with the oil that we still had. Fuel oil, I discovered, was never the big input into farming. The big input was chemicals. Nitrogen fertiliser was the biggest item of these – and where were farmers going to get that from? There was very little available, and when that was gone there would be none. The only substitute for it, apparently, would be dung – the manure from animals. But in East Anglia there were few animals. The few huge factory farms in the area, that had kept thousands of animals and birds under intensive conditions (in what many people called "Belsen houses") simply collapsed. When the electricity cut out so did the air pumps in the hen battery houses and the hens simply died of suffocation. Great waves of disease swept through the intensive pig units. The huge supplies of food-stuffs, most of which came from abroad anyway, were cut off. Millions of birds and animals died.

I remember at one of these farmers' meetings a man with a beard got up and made a suggestion. It was that the land should be subdivided into many small plots and given out to smallholders. Such people, he said, would be better able to return to labour-intensive agriculture. (I remember he used an old-fashioned word – husbandry) and practice a mixed farming that would return animal manure to the land, and keep animals in more natural conditions in which they would not die from disease or famine.

I liked this man's suggestion but I remember the other farmers who were present – all managers or owners of enormous mechanised farms around Bury St. Edmunds – just laughing at the man and refusing to take him seriously at all. Months later I had the embarrassing duty of sentencing this same bearded man to six months in Breckland. A patrol of mine had visited his farm. It was only fifteen acres but he had stashed away on it fine vegetables, eggs, bacon and ham, smoked sausages, butter and cheese, a ton of good wheat and several barrels of home-brewed beer. When my men came to take all this away he actually threatened a lance corporal with a pitch fork! I sometimes look back on it all and remember the Greek saying: *Whom the Gods wish to destroy they first make mad!* Assuredly, to destroy the goose that laid the golden eggs – the farmer – was mad.

Reports came back from my First Battalion to say that they had made contact with territorials the other side of Randersfield. I only mention this because it had a bearing on this book. The "terriers" seemed to have good control of the area between Randersfield and the sea and they expressed willingness to go on controlling there until the regular army was ready to take over and to allow our lorries in to take away food as required.

As my command was stretched to the limit at the time I decided to let them be, until the situation was sufficiently under control to allow us to extend our area. We made similar arrangements in many other peripheral areas. I was determined, however, to carry out the orders of High Command that these autonomous areas should not be allowed to survive for too long.

The High Command, by the way, was at Birmingham University. From here the intention was to rule all England. All of us in the army were convinced that England must one day only have one government and the fact that Northern Command was slow in acknowledging the authority of General Wicklow did not worry us much. We believed they soon would. As for the Welsh – Wicklow made it quite clear to all of us that he intended to invade that country and extend central government to it again. But obviously this would have to wait. And I can say honestly, here and now, that I was never in favour of such an idea at all.

Chapter Seventeen

by Bob Hurlock

For the first two days, when we got to Gretford, we rested, sorted ourselves out, looked around. I'll never forget that first hot bath.

The very fact of being free, temporarily, of fear, free from the excitement of hiding, moving, fighting, made one feel light-headed. Then reaction set in. For me at least. I began to think of what I had lost. For the first time, I think, was I really able to feel grief. I walked, one evening, along the road to Cragpit. I stood and looked at our home from the distance. I had not the heart to go into it. I felt I had not the heart to do anything. Even revenge no longer appealed to me. Then I thought – I know what Jessie would have had me do. Go back and try and sort things out so that one little corner of England, at least, was fit to live in. I am trying to make this the story of what happened to our bit of England: I have not dwelt much on my own thoughts or feelings. I can only say that – right from the time that I had heard the news about my family from the night-nurse in the Maltings hospital I had felt as though my heart was full of gall. In battle – in flight – in defeat and success – there was that dull, lead weight, pressing on my heart. There was no elation.

But still there was no time to grieve. Now that the army had gone we could give people back their requisitioned houses, and there was room for us to make our headquarters. We moved the refugees out of the big house opposite *The Crown* and set up

offices in there. We transferred them to my house, which I could
not bear to enter. I lodged with a dear old lady who lived in a
little cottage. *The Crown* was completely wrecked; so were the
old London Farming offices. As for Brown – he went away with
the troops, and we never saw him again.

It was urgently necessary to set up some sort of government.

Bill Smithers and Harry Blendover had both been taken by the
army. It was known that they had been in our first council and
therefore they were under suspicion anyway and we had left
Harry in the forest when we drove away. Harry we never saw
again; Bill came back later with the released prisoners from
Breckland.

The day after we had entered the little town we had a meeting
in the big room at *The King's Head*. There were fourteen of us
there: our ten platoon commanders; Eli, who would never take
command of a platoon in the forest – he liked to operate by
himself; the doctor; Dike; and me. We had a bottle of Scotch on
the table; the enemy, in their hurry to get away, had left even
that.

I made a little speech. "We've got them out," I said, "but mark
my words – they'll be back. We haven't finished with 'em."

"Dam' right we in't," said Dike.

"First thing we got to do," said Eli, "is hang all them traitors –
Brown and that lot. There's a bit of vermin-destruction got to be
done."

There were some "hear! hears!"

"Well I don't know what the rest of you think," I said. "And I
don't give a dam'. We haven't got time for much democracy at
the moment – I'm going to be a dictator for a month or two and
you can do what you like together. And the first thing I'm
dictating is this. There is to be no hounding down of traitors.
There are to be no recriminations. If Brown is here – I have an
idea he's vamoosed – but if he's here he'll be treated exactly like
everybody else . . ."

There was a chorus of protest from some, led by Eli, but Dike
and one or two of the older ones agreed. "Save-Soul" Jones even

cried: "Amen to that!"

After everybody had shouted for a while, Dike bellowed: "Order!" and I made myself heard.

"Listen," I said. "We've got a hell of a lot to do. People are damned hungry. We've got hardly any animals left – for breeding let alone for slaughter. And it's thanks to Master Brown I might say we've got any . . ."

"That bastard!"

"Yes all right – but he did fight with the army to keep as many head of stock as they'd let him. He also fought with them to retain some grain, and potatoes. We've got some grub – but not much. We must farm very skilfully if we're not going to starve next winter. Remember – we're cut off. We can't go looting around the countryside. We're blockaded. Another thing – we are still surrounded by enemies. You can be damned sure that they'll be back . . ."

"We'll give 'em what they got before!" said Eli. "We still got some medicine in the bottle."

"Yes – but we want to be prepared to do it. Then, come Michaelmas, we must dish out the land again. This time for good. There are going to be no more tractors – this time it's final. So we haven't got time for hunting out our own people. And where does it stop? If you shoot a man who you know was a traitor – where does it stop? No – there is to be no naming of traitors."

"Put it to the vote!"

"I'm damned if I will. I've told you there ain't going to be no democracy round here!"

"Go on!" said Dike. "Put it to the vote. Come on – hands up them that agree with the Skipper!"

Ten hands went up. Eli's was not among them.

"Now then," I said. "Dike! You're head of the army."

"Me?"

"Yes. You're a good tactician. And do you know who you're going to have as adjutant? You're going to have Major Dugdale."

"Him? That bastard? He's one we could well do without."

"He is going to stay here in Gretford and organise his
territorials again. He was good at doing that. He can get the men
together, see they are armed and have ammunition, see there are
stores for them. You will be in command of them and it's up to
you to repulse the foe. Now we're not arguing. Bill Smithers, if
he gets back from the nick, will be Minister of Animal
Husbandry."

"Cripes!"

"It will be his job to see that every breeding animal in this
district is cared for, and breeds," there were ribald shouts at this.
"We must feed them even if humans go short. Bob Randle – you
have been a farmer most of your life – you will be Minister of
Agriculture. You will see that the miserable bit of crops that
London Farming did manage to grow this year are harvested.
Peter Smithers – you are Minister of Fish. It's up to you to see
that your fellow fishermen have everything they need that we can
supply 'em with. I know we can't get a lot of gear but you'll
have to make do with what we can get. We'll talk about fish
weirs afterwards. Your forefathers used to use them. John
Hughes – you were Minister of Industry before – you are again.
You'll have to soft-peddle, I fancy, until we get the harvest in.
Sam Packard – you were a "schoolie" – you'll be Minister of
Education. You'll see that the kids go to school. And you'll have
to see that they get taught a hell of a lot beside the Three Rs. But
you'll have to wait until after harvest too. John Lloyd – you were
going to study Law – you're Minister of Justice. And your father
can be judge. He'd love that. Doc – you're Health. That's all the
government. Now I didn't leave the rest of you out because
you're no good. I left you out because you are good soldiers.
We're all going to be armed in this new Jerusalem, but most of
us are going to go about our business. But we want a small
standing army – thirty men perhaps – on parade all the time to
bear the brunt. You're going to be it."

Eli spoke up. "Cap'n," he said. "Do you mind if I go off and
shoot some more o' them soldiers? I in't shot half enough yet."

I thought for a moment. "We'll talk about that afterwards,"

I said. And that was that. I set myself up as a little dictator. I didn't see anything else that would work.

Everybody seemed happy enough about these arrangements. We called for some more whisky, a melodeon was fetched from somewhere. Other habitués of *The King's Head* came in, and with the exception of "Save-Soul" Jones we all got drunk.

The government, as it turned out, worked very well indeed.

Dugdale, who had thought he might be shot, was only too happy to set about organising his Home Guard, as we decided to call it. Every able-bodied man who could be given a weapon was in it; they were trained a little, organised into units, and told where to go and what to do in an emergency.

The harvest was very ticklish.

The result was crops of scarcely believable meagreness. Miserable wheat and barley a few inches high. I was delighted to see that on those areas of my own farm which had got sown with seed, the crops were excellent. But my farm had been *farmed* – right along. Farmyard manure, ploughed-in leys, ploughed-in green-manure crops – my land was in good heart and would have grown crops for years with nothing else put in it.

But that was why I was so desperately anxious to increase the head of stock in the district. In the absence of artificial fertilisers – we had to return to horn-and-corn farming if we were not to starve.

There was one factor that I missed sorely, and that was Mick Miller and his sailing barge. He had sailed away, apparently soon after I had been arrested, and had not come back again. The barge had been seen sailing past several times, but she had stood well out and had not come in. I told our fishermen, who still had enough drift-nets to bring in a huge supply of long-shore herring that year (it was a bumper year presumably because of the cessation of trawling for herring by big ships) to keep a look out for the *Suffolkman*, but they did not see her again. She would have been useful.

As for Eli, he came to me with three other men, all hard-cases like himself, and asked for permission to go and shoot soldiers.

I told him he could – if he went right over to the Breckland side. "Don't mess about here, Eli," I said. "It'll only disturb the peace and stir things up and we can't afford that until we're better sorted out. Wait 'til we've divided out the land, got some good crops coming in, got people more on our side here – then we'll have a whack at 'em. Don't worry. Meanwhile you can do us a lot of good by beating 'em up in the Brecklands – keeping their attention away from here. Join up with some of those Fen boys. Try to get them to help you rescue all those poor chaps in the prison camps. Time they were out."

He agreed to do this, and he and his little gang took bicycles across the land bridge and we only heard rumours of them for several months.

Foreign affairs began to make themselves felt. We started getting people coming to us from other pockets of resistance up and down the East Coast asking for help against the thieving army. Most of them came to us along the coast by boat. Would we arm them? Send help to them? If things went on as they were going they would all starve, they said.

For the army simply could not organise farming under the new conditions. They still tried to farm on the old extractive basis, but they could not do it because they had none of the agricultural chemicals – and fewer and fewer machines. Also they didn't know how to. They still tried to farm the land through the big farming companies, such as London Farming, when the only possible way would have been to have farmed on a peasant basis. They always managed to alienate the sympathies of the people who could have shown them how to do it: the true country people: people they would have referred to contemptuously as "yokels", or at best – "the locals".

We did help these strangers as much as we could. We sent arms to them in boats – as many as we could spare. They were still managing to get a little diesel oil for their fishing boats – from the army of course. Our fishermen at Shoreness had pulled off their propellers, keeping their engines in as ballast, and had improvised sails out of adapted yacht sails. Some were purloining the many deserted yachts.

We helped the strangers because we had no intention of leaving our quarrel with the army as it was. We intended to attack them again, after we had organised our little state and made that secure. For we knew that as long as the army held power in other parts of the country they were a menace to us. If they really tried, surely they could crack our little nut? At least they could force us to take to the woods again. If they settled their troubles in the rest of the country – defeated the Fenmen – then our turn would come. And so we were glad to hear of little gangs of outlaws in woods other than ours.

As the months went by our little republic took shape.

People took over their holdings of land again, and really started to farm them. In default of manure, leaf-mould was carried from the woods, sea-weed from the shore. Some people didn't take holdings, but did other jobs. The bumper herring harvest that autumn was our salvation. There was good protein food for all of us – for many months because we salted a lot. There were the heads and guts for the pigs. The herrings were a godsend.

Some people took to industries. John Hughes, the young geology student, was magnificent. He got together a team of people, and together they devised and set up all sorts of successful enterprises.

Charcoal for example. Wood was bulky, and hard to carry without mechanical or animal transport. Charcoal was light and small in bulk for the heat it gave. They set up a charcoal-burning industry in the woods.

Sugar. They worked out a way of extracting this from sugar beet, using wood as fuel. A by-product was very good rum, for they set up a distillery.

Salt. There was plenty of drift-wood always on our beach. They set people to evaporating the sea-water with drift-wood fires.

Bricks. They learnt anew how to burn bricks with wood.

Pottery. There was a girl who had always made pots in Gretford: she was set to starting an industry for the making of

wood-fired earthenware. True, there was for the time no shortage
of such articles; but it was felt that a shortage would come. And
the things they made were far ahead of the machine-made rubbish
that we had been used to, aesthetically that is.

Leather tanning and bootmaking. Carding and spinning wool
and weaving. Pilot industries, as it were, were set up in all these.
We managed to get some flax seeds from a town to the north
(like a lot of other things in exchange for ammunition). This we
planted with the idea of eventually starting a linen and flax
industry to say nothing of growing linseed for oil.

One problem that we could not solve that first winter was light.
Our little stores of oil soon ran out. There were not enough sheep
or cattle to kill for animal fat, with which we could have made
candles or rush-lights. We sat by large fires (we were never short
of wood – if we liked to go and get it) and went to bed early.
Water, too, could no longer be pumped. People dug wells near
their houses to solve this problem. Grinding corn was another
thing. Under Hughes' tireless direction a windmill was built –
and she worked! She took a year to build, though, and meanwhile
we soaked our wheat, and boiled it, or ground it with stones, or
such things as coffee-grinders.

Naturally there was great discomfort that first year, to people
used to everything happening when you flicked a switch. Plenty
of people longed for the army back – and the oil. Many of the ex-
city people would have revolted. They didn't because we kept
our eyes well open. Others, I believe, really enjoyed themselves.
It was fun to them – and an adventure. For the first time in their
lives they were free from all the petty worries of big civilisation.
They still had to keep up with the Jones's but only in simple
things – like a good crop of winter greens in their gardens. For
the first time in their lives they had the fun of being dependent on
themselves.

While talking of greens – one legacy that Jessie had left us
were her seeds. Her plants grew. By enormous luck the officer
who had been given our house to live in had been a keen
gardener, and he had seen the sense of trying to propagate seeds.

He had caused his men to tend the plants, and when we took over again they were all growing well. The seeds that we were able to save, and propagate further, were of enormous value.

Cragpit Farm was gradually emptied of its orphans, for the policy was to farm them all out to private people. Many of them had it pretty rough, the poor little devils, because there was more work to be done than everybody could do – but it was a rough world they were in and they were, like us, lucky to be alive. The simple country kindness of the Suffolk people was enough to ensure that most of them were treated well. Many of them – particularly the younger ones – merged in completely with the families they were given to.

When the last one went I walked down to look at our old home. I had suddenly had a whim that Jessie would have liked me to have carried the farm on: with, perhaps, the six orphan children who had come to live with us before our disaster. Dickie Quantrill had several times suggested it to me.

I was dying to hand over the government. I hated politics: even unusual ones.

It was a bright, clear spring day. I remembered that it was a year to the day since we fired our first shot in the war against the army.

The house was quite empty: the last of the orphans, with the women who had looked after them, had left that day. The place had been well cared for. I was glad that I had not bazookaed it, as I had sometimes thought of doing, when the army were there.

Going into the garden, with its enclosing brick wall, was unbearably sad for me. I remembered little incidents from the past – Jeannie first standing up as a baby by that window – the kids building a house in the big ash tree – I could still see some bits of wood nailed up there. I imagined I could hear the voices of the children as they played in the bushes – or rode their ponies over in the paddock. There was Susan's old tricycle rusted up now. Cast aside in the shrubbery.

I entered by the conservatory. There were my Jessie's careful plants – I remembered the very day she had planted them out so carefully, so lovingly. I remember her saying: "If we only have the right seeds, Bear, we can survive."

I looked into the living-room. I expected to hear her voice. "Bear – where are you? Tea-time darling Bear!"

No, no – I couldn't. Never! I could not live in that house again. I would be mad – in a fortnight. It was full of ghosts.

Work was the only thing. I must go back – quickly – to my politics. I must strengthen my little state. And I must hit the enemy again – when I was better prepared. Kill the bastards – as many as I could! But even as I thought that, I fancied I heard her voice saying: "No Bear – don't think like that. They're only people like the rest of us you know. They may have got a bit muddled – bad men have got to the top. But the men underneath can't help it. They're only puzzled – not knowing what to do for the best . . ."

I was walking quickly along the drive – away from the house where I had spent the happiest years of my life. Inside my head it seemed as if a whirlwind was blowing. The mental pain that I was suffering was a physical thing – like a steel band tightening about my skull. I was afraid of going mad.

I saw someone – heard a voice. It was the village idiot. The Gretford village idiot. All good villages have an idiot. Ours spent a lot of time wandering about alone, down on the marshes.

"Have you been looking at your house Captain?" he said, in his idiotic way.

I thought of going on – not replying. Then – like a blow – I thought of what Jessie would have said to that. She was always kind to the poor idiot. She was angry once because I was impatient with him.

I stopped. "Yes," I said. "That is – it was my house – once."

"They took your wife away," said the village idiot.

"Yes."

"And your children."

"Yes."

"They took them – down there . . ."

"Where?"

"Down there – to the water."

"To the water?"

"Yes – to the water."

"Who took them?"

"Some soldiers. The officer who used to swear so – and who gave me cigarettes."

"Captain Giles? What did they do to them?"

"They went away in the ship. The big ship with sails. The one wot brought you the oil."

"My God! Are you sure? Are you sure?"

"Have you got any cigarettes, Captain?"

"Are you sure they went in the barge? Why – why the hell did you never tell anybody this before?"

"Nobody ever asked me, Captain."

But I only just heard the last remark. I was running flat out in the direction of Gretford.

Chapter Eighteen

by Bob Hurlock

Well, since nothing will make Dickie tell this I'll have to do it. Of course, when I was already to sail the wind swung round and blew a gale. I was held up for three days, during which I nearly went mad.

Young Dickie Quantrill asked to come with me. He had always been a sailorman. He and another chap had owned a boat together. We picked the most suitable of the little yachts that lay at Shore-end: a little sailing cabin cruiser – I know nothing about boats so am probably even getting the jargon wrong. We victualled her for a fortnight – and then it blew this gale. And I thought it would never stop.

The gale was probably just as well, actually, for it gave me time to hand over the reins, to put a small matter very pompously, of government. There seemed to me to be endless details to be attended to, until one day Dike (who was to be in charge of the District) said to me: "Blast Bor! You fare to think the grass can't grow while you're away. Allow us a little sense!" And I realised that I was not indispensable. They would probably get along better without me.

At last the wind changed – moderated – veered west – then north-west. Dike and the rest of them came down to the shore to see us off. We sat in the little cabin, or about the deck, drinking rum until the tide was right, then – with shouted wishes of good luck, the people who were saying good-bye went ashore; Dickie got the anchor up, and he and I together urged the little vessel down the estuary on the ebb tide, making use of two big oars, which he called "sweeps".

Once outside we set our sails – Dickie giving orders in a very seaman-like manner and me obeying them in a very unseaman-like one – and started sailing, very pleasantly, south along the coast. The sea was calm, I was not seasick. Dickie seemed to know what he was doing.

We passed various landmarks along the coast. At Aldeburgh we saw cars moving ashore, so we knew the army was there. We stood well out. We could see that the *Suffolkman* was not in the Alde or Ore: if she had been we would have seen her masts.

Off Bawdsey we found fishing boats, trawling with engines. We went alongside one. I vaguely knew the skipper – having seen him in the pub.

"Seen the *Suffolkman*?" I asked, as we came alongside.

"She came by here several months ago," the man said. "And the army sent a motor boat after her. But when the motor boat came alongside the chaps on the barge fired at her with one o' them bazooka things and dam' nigh blew her out of the water! That was gone within a few minutes. Then the barge headed out to sea and we in't seen her since."

"Oh," I said. "Where do you get your oil from?"

"Army let us have it. But I'd rather they kep' their oil and we keep our fish. We'd muddle along somehow. They take the bloomin' lot. They leave us just enough fish for half a fry-up for the missus and kids – and they give us such a miserable little bit of rotten ol' flour and rotten tatties as you can't imagine. If me and my mate didn't have a fry-up at sea here – and have a good tuck in afore we take the catch ashore – I'm sure we'd never keep a'gooin'."

"Do you reckon the army's a good thing?"

"No that I don't. We'd be far better off without 'em. Don't you come from Gretford way mister? I think I see you there in the old *Barge* at Yeldham Ferry once or twice."

"That you did."

"Haven't you kicked the army out of round about there? We hear odd rumours."

"We have kicked 'em out. And we'll keep 'em out."

"I wish we could do that about here. They're nothing but a lot of scrim-shankers. They live on the work of other people."

"Do your lot come from Willingham?"

"They come under that bunch. They all come from the Sheers."

"Are the army in Essex?"

"I don't reckon they are, from what I can hear of it. They got their own government up that way – Walton and Clacton and all like that way."

"Come on Cap'n – we're bashing her to pieces!" came from Dickie, who had been trying desperately to keep the two boats apart.

"Here's an old roka," said the fisherman, and he threw a skate aboard us. If nothing else had improved since the CRASH – the fishing had. Now that there were no big trawlers the sea seemed to have come alive with fish.

The wind had northered – and freshened – and we spun along. Off Harwich we spoke a rowing boat (I hope I am using the correct nautical terms). "Is the *Suffolkman* in there?" I shouted.

"No she isn't!" shouted one of the boatmen. And he waved his arm vaguely southwards. We were out of hail before we could indulge in much detail.

The next hole in the land was Hamford Water, but we decided to give that a miss. There was nothing for a barge to go for in there.

We held on past the high bluff headland of the Naze.

Ripping along over the sparkling water on that superb December day was an experience I shall never forget. Why, I wondered, had I never tried this activity before? My year in the bush had hardened me to cold in an amazing manner. The little boat sliced along in the bright sunshine, riding the waves that came rushing up from astern, the land looked beautiful: the green Naze stood up against the blue sky – the little town of Walton, then the brown crumbling cliffs, then Frinton, looking bright and deserted, then, when darkness was falling quickly, Clacton came into view. The merest sprinkling of lights came up ashore.

"We'll try to make Brightlingsea," said Dickie. "We've a fair wind. I don't want to be out at night. That's going to blow up I misdoubt and we must remember – there are no lights now."

Of course. I had not thought of that. All the hundreds of lighted buoys and light-ships of the Thames Estuary: all out now.

It became quite dark, but Dickie, by some mariner's instinct that I could not understand, navigated our way into the River Colne, and sailed right into Brightlingsea Creek.

Brightlingsea, I was surprised to find, was moderately well lighted with electric lights.

"Shall we go ashore?" said Dickie. "Shall we risk it?"

"Come on," I said. "I don't think we'll find Midlanders here. Anyway, nobody'll know who we are."

We went ashore in the dinghy. At the top of the hard was a big pub, with lights on. Electric lights too. We entered it.

It was surprisingly full.

We had brought some money with us: ordinary money such as we all used before the CRASH.

"Two pints of twos," I said. And I flung down a ten pound note.

The landlady looked at it. "That's no good," she said. "No good round here."

"It's all I've got," I said. "Except some Gretford money. We have our own money where I come from."

"So do we here," she said. "It got ridiculous, after the CRASH. There was people with a million pounds in the bank – and they hadn't got a penny in their pockets. There was others who had a thousand or two in cash. Nobody knew what anything was worth anymore. Then it got so no-one would sell anything for money – money didn't seem to be worth nothing. So then we had this here government of Tendring Hundred and they printed their own money – on top of the old money. Look . . ."

she showed us a pound note which had been sur-printed with the words: 'Tendring Hundred Currency' and a complicated scroll design. "That was a pound. It now buys a pint of beer. But if it wasn't sur-printed it wouldn't buy a thing."

"Well – we can't have a drink then," I said.

"Here you are mate – have one on me," said a man who was standing near the bar.

"That's very kind of you."

We sat down at a table together.

"We are looking for a barge called the *Suffolkman*," I said.

Suffolkman, she come in here sometimes," said the man. "She bring a load of coal sometimes – or she brought one at least. Where she is now I don't know. Mick Miller, eh? He's a lucky man. Having a sailing ship. Come into his own again I reckon."

I told him where we came from. "How have you got on round here?" I asked. "Since the CRASH."

"Oh – well – not too badly," he said. "I was a Londoner really – used to come here for weekends. Was here when the CRASH came. I've got a job at the shipyard here now. We're trying to build sailing barges – out of steel. We've got plenty of plate – had it left over – but there's difficulties. But I think we'll get a couple built – if not more. They'll be worth their weight in gold."

"Where does your grub come from?"

"Farmers. We've managed to keep the army out of here."

"You didn't get the army?"

"No – we had several troops stationed about here – but they didn't take charge. They took their orders from the civil power, as it were."

"And what is that?"

"Well after the CRASH we got together around here – and eventually decided to form a local government for what we called the Tendring Hundred. Headquarters are at Weeley actually. It seems to work quite well."

"How do you get electric light?"

"Well – we've managed here at Brightlingsea to get some steam engines going. Run on coal. Only public houses – government offices – places of important work – have light though. That's why this pub's so full. People don't want to sit home in the dark."

I got him, and others, there, to tell me how their part of the country worked.

Their farms, it appeared, had not been sub-divided. Pre-CRASH ownership had never been challenged, in anything. If people wanted food they had to buy it – with the new currency.

"And the only way to get money for food is to work," said a man. "And except for one or two of the lucky ones the only work is on the farms. You get men who were millionaires out in the fields hoeing all day. Their millions were in the bank – they're worth nothing now. They want food – the farmers have the food – and the money – so they have to go to the farmers and ask for work, anything. And the farmers need labour – no machines now. No more oil. It works all right, I suppose, but it's unfair. The farmers are the lords of everything."

"Who pays for the ship-building?"

"Well – farmers again. The farmers are the bosses – no doubt about that. A few farmers have floated a company to build these barges. They want to trade with them. Foreign parts – like Kent and Suffolk. Sound funny don't it? – but that's how it's got."

"What's happened in Kent?"

"Oh – they're better off down there. Got their own coal mines for one thing. Big stocks of coal. And big towns weren't hit so bad. Medway Towns suffered a lot of starvation. They're more organised there. Plenty of grub too – Navy helps organise 'em."

"Do you get people coming in from outside? Looting and that?"

"We're beginning to. Not here but in the more westerly parts. But we've got our little bit of army – they deal with that – they've had a set-to with your Midland army once or twice."

"One thing I think ought to be changed," said one man, "is the farmers having the lot."

"Oh that's got to be changed!" said the other. "You see – the farmers now have everything. Every single thing. It's not fair you know. The rest of us are no better than slaves, really. If you own land – you get the best of everything and needn't do any work. If you don't you're nowhere. It's not fair you know. After all – plenty of us owned big businesses before the CRASH – and we start with nothing now but what we stand up in. Plenty were professional men – worked hard all their lives – now they're scratching about with a hoe for a bare living. It's got to be changed."

"Trouble is," said the other chap, "it's written into our constitution – existing property rights shall be held valid whatever happens."

"You see – they were afraid of anarchy – if once property rights weren't respected. We all were."

"But it's got to be changed."

But, how ever badly off these non-farmers were, beer flowed freely enough. There seemed to be no shortage of that, and it was good beer: much better than the chemically-tasting muck we had all had to get used to before the CRASH.

We discovered that Brightlingsea was quite a busy port. There were still motor barges moving about: barge skippers had access to stores of oil that other people knew little about. By making use of the tides they could make their voyages with very little use of the engine at all. Most motor barges had improvised sails, too, and it was obvious that sail would gradually oust the motors. Trade was brisk between Kent and Essex, and barges had even been "over the other side".

"How do the Dutch and Belgians fare?" I asked.

"Well that's hard to say," said the skipper I was talking to. "It's hard rightly to understand them – make out what's going on. They were civil – I took them a load of stuff from London – stuff out of basements – tea and coffee and all such as that – and they took it and I brought back a load of salt herrings and onions and a few things we are short of over here. When I say a load – not a quarter of a load. There's really not much that they've got that we want or vice versa. I shan't go again."

"Why don't you come north – our way?"

"Well – we've been warned to stay clear of this blasted army, the Midland lot. They say they're the government of England and everybody comes under them. They'd seize a barge, as like as not. What have you got that we would want?"

"We've got salt herrings galore. And we've got pine wood galore. That's all – at the moment." And I told them about our little republic of Gretford District. They expressed their sympathy, and wished us well in our struggle against the Midland army.

But none of them could give us news of the *Suffolkman*. "I know she's not in Kent," said one. "I've just come from Dover – I'd have heard of her. Not Whitstable side either."

"I've just come down London River," said another. "She's not up there."

"I reckon she's north. Down Humber way – after coal. That's where she'll be."

It was most disappointing. It seemed like looking for a needle in a haystack. Finally I decided that the only thing to do was to sail "down north" to the Humber – and either meet her on the way, or find her there.

"You'll have to wait for a change of wind," said a bargeman.

And a change of wind there was. The next day the breeze had set back to south-easterly, and we sailed – against the advice of the bargemen ashore – but Dickie was young and rash and I was desperate. I knew not the dangers.

It was rough outside, and we got a terrible dusting in the mouth of the Colne. We were both soaked with spray. When we turned the corner to reach along the coast, however, it was easier, for the wind was on our beam. By the time we got to Walton Pier, however, a full gale was blowing. We had to reef right down.

Dickie was making a fine attempt to disguise the fact that he was rattled.

"We'll have to run for somewhere," he said.

"Where? We can't go to Harwich. The army are there. They'll pinch the boat and jail us."

"We must go in somewhere."

"We can't."

"It's blowing up for a real gale. When the tide turns and we get wind against tide it'll be a real stinker. She in't a big boat."

"Where can we go to?"

"I know – I've never been in there – but what about Walton Backwaters?"

"Hamford Water do you mean? That's what it's called on the map. You might be right – army might not be there. We could try."

We accordingly sailed in to the mouth of the wide estuary of the Hamford Water (I had maps with me), turned left into the Walton Channel and Dickie nosed the boat right up against the steep-banked sandy shore of Stone Point. This is the tip of a long narrow spit of ground, that divided the estuary known as Hamford water (or the Backwaters in local talk) from the sea.

There was nobody there. There was just the remains of an old hut.

We went ashore, found some driftwood, lit a fire, and cooked the skate the fisherman had given us the day before. We had fried potatoes with it and it was delicious.

Just as the sun was setting the sky cleared somewhat. There was a fine sunset over the water and the saltings. I got up from our blazing fire (which we had lit in the lee of the broken hut) and walked away from the glare of it so that I could enjoy the sunset. Thoughts of Jessie filled my mind. She had loved the sunset. She used to annoy me sometimes when I was busy doing something she would suddenly come rushing in: "Bear! Bear! Come and look! Quick!"

And all it was was the sunset, like any other sunset.

I had been looking at the object silhouetted against the sunset for some moments before it registered. I was just thinking: "Who in my younger days, could have imagined the Essex marshes without the mast and sprit of a . . ."

Sailing barge! But that's what we were here to look for.

"Dickie!" I shouted. "Get aboard! She's there – we've found her!"

Dickie jumped up and looked too. He scrambled aboard and got the sails up. I put the anchor aboard – shoved her nose off – and pulled myself over. Dickie put the helm up and we sailed straight for the West Water: that wide, short channel that runs up the middle of the Hamford Water.

I knew I should find Jessie and the children now. I felt certain of it. They might not be at the barge – but they would be somewhere – alive.

My pent-up excitement was unbearable. I wanted the little boat to fly. She was moving quite fast – but she couldn't have moved fast enough for me. Suddenly she slowed down – there was a slithering noise – she stopped!

"We're on the putty," said Dickie.

We both pushed and shoved with the two big sweeps, or oars. The oars just went into the mud. We were high and dry – on the spit that runs our between the Walton Channel and West Water. We could not move her.

"Would it be any good if I jumped overboard?" I said.

"You'd freeze yourself to dead and do no good at all," said Dickie.

"What shall we do?"

"There's nothing we can do."

"I thought you were a bloody yachtsman!"

"Sorry Cap! I'm not a magician!"

"Oh don't be a fool. You've done dam' well, Dickie. We'll just have to be patient, that's all." The tide had already gone down a lot, leaving us heeling over at a slight angle. We had chosen a boat that could, as Dickie put it, "take the ground".

"How long will it be until we float again?"

"Eight hours – at least. It's near the top of the tide."

So I had to contain my impatience as best I could. We could not even go ashore. The mud was far too soft.

Before it got quite dark we could see the figure of a man standing on the sea wall of Horsey Island. He was looking at us. I thought of speaking to him – then I thought better of it. He went away. I didn't like it at all. Who was he? Where had he gone? Who would he tell?

We slept in the little cabin that night – at least Dickie slept: I only had snatches. I felt like a fly stuck on a spider's web.

It was still dark when we floated (or fleeted as Dickie said). I could feel her swinging, and I rushed up on deck. The wind had dropped: there was a light breeze from the east.

The sky was clear and starry.

I woke Dickie. We pulled the mainsail up, and the anchor. We fleeted quietly away on the breeze and the flooding tide – up the quiet water, slowly, pleasantly, the wind, or gale, if it was one, had died down. I decided I liked yachting. "I'm going to do more of it," I said.

The low shore of Horsey Island drifted by to the left of us. We turned left up a little creek that ran between Horsey Island and Skipper's Island. The barge was there: we could see her noble spars and rigging and brailed sails against the stars.

We bumped gently alongside. We heard a hatch-cover slide back aft. A man came on deck. "Can you tell me where I can find the nearest yacht club?" I drawled.

"Who the hell's that!" said Mick Miller. He had a gun in his hands.

"It's me you old barnacle!"

"Who's me . . . why it's Bob! Good God, I thought you were the old man of the sea! Come aboard you silly bugger – young Dickie too – my God we thought you were dead and done with years ago. Come aboard – your wife's ashore on the island there – all the kids – fit and well – they all thought you were dead though. Come on – come aboard!"

"I think I'll – I think I'll go and find Jessie."

"Well – don't go until it comes light. They're living in the cottage over by the farm – it's about a mile and very difficult to find your way over the marshes. Also people about here are a bit sharp with the trigger. You might get a bullet through your guts. Come below and have a cup of tea."

"Tea? Where the hell do you get tea?"

"Oh – I've been trading up the London River lately. The place is dead – but it's surprising what you can find if you scrabble about among the ruins. Lots of the stuff in cellars and all. I don't scrabble but I trade with them that do. Come below."

Down in Mick's little cabin a hot coal fire was burning and an oil lamp was on. It was snug and comfortable, and safe and secure. Of Mick's female crew – two pretty girls, one had married Mick. That was Meg. The other lived with a boy named Charlie up in the fo'c'sle. She was the Mate, Mick told me, Charlie was the cook.

Mick made tea. It was wonderful.

"There are people living among the ruins of London like rats in rubble," he said. "And they live on what they can scrounge among the ruins and by trading with people like me who come in from the countryside. We take 'em country produce: they give us tinned tea and stuff."

"Tell us what happened to you. How did Jessie come here?"

"Well – after that army came in and you got pinched – I didn't like the look of things you know. I wondered what I could do to help you – there was nothing I could think of. I thought whatever I did I'd got to stick to the barge. I believe that's important you know. There's been quite a lot of traffic with motor barges you know – even one or two steam things dodging about but they're very rare. But the oil is running out quickly. I don't think we'll see many more motor boats about. Certainly not unless a few tankers started coming in from the east and I can't see that happening. It looks as though the *Suffolkman* is going to be about the only cargo ship left working soon. So I must look after her. There's nobody else could sail her."

"Well tell us what happened."

"Well I was already making up my mind to up-sticks and get out of it – when that Hugh Giles fellow – you remember – the captain who swore so much? Great friend of yours. Well he came along in the middle of the night – we were lying in the mud-berth beside your farm – he came along with four other soldiers – they'd all deserted – and he had your missus and kids with him – and Mrs Woolpit. They'd been shut up in some hospital or somewhere – they'd been kicked out of their houses to make

room for army chaps – so I suppose they'd got to put 'em
somewhere. Giles was sent to shoot them. I think they wanted
him to refuse so they could court-martial him. So he said he
would – went and got 'em and brought them down to my barge.
So Giles said would I sail away with the lot of them – up south –
anywhere out of it – and I did. Luckily we had an off-shore wind
that night – just the wind we wanted – we hauled up our topsail
and were away before light. I knew of this place – often thought
it would make a good hidey-hole. So here we came. And we've
been based here ever since."

"What does Jessie do?"

"She lives in one of the two cottages over on Horsey Island.
I'll take you there as soon as it gets light. She and the kids all
work for the farmer there. Man named Eagle. He's a dam' good
chap. They feed well – I bring them coal and paraffin – and tea
and coffee and things like that – they're very well off. There's
one thing I must tell you. Robin's not there."

"Where's Robin?"

"He went to look for you. Didn't tell his mother – left her a
note. Got on a bike and pushed off. The note said he was going
to the Brecklands, wherever that is, because that's where you
were a prisoner. And he's never come back again. Giles too –
Captain Giles – he went away too.

This alarmed me. After all, Robin was only twelve years old. I
looked through the skylight above us – and saw that dawn was
breaking.

"Come on," I said.

Mike dressed, slowly, and he and I went up and got down into
his boat. Dickie decided to lie down in the cabin of the barge and
have a sleep.

Mike sculled us over to the Horsey Island shore. There was a
hard there, near where we anchored the boat. Mike led the way
over the sea-wall and across the marshes of the island.

We could hear cocks crowing and dogs barking as we
approached the farmhouse. The double cottage stood nearby, and
we went to the back door. Inside I could see a pretty girl washing

her face at the scullery sink. It was Diana.

She looked up and saw me – and looked frightened. Then she saw Mike. I knocked on the door.

It opened – again that look of non-recognition from Diana – and then: "Daddy!"

Her screams brought the others. Mike left us to it. I was practically carried into the little living-room, and sat down, and people wept, and the whole scene was very emotional and quite un-English. Certainly not the way you expect an English farmer's family to carry on.

Chapter Nineteen

by Jessie Hurlock

Oh gee, oh my, I just cannot describe what it felt like having my old Bear back again and knowing the silly old fool was alive!

The girls got us all a good English breakfast – good smoked bacon and new-laid eggs and wholemeal bread and coffee that dear old Mick had brought down from London in his barge – and then we went to milk the cows. Charlie Eagle didn't want us to but of course we did. And all the time I sat pulling at old Fillpail's teats great shudders would keep going through me and I'd start to blub. I just couldn't believe it – I had been sure Bob was dead.

The girls helped Elsie make cheese while I went for a long walk with Bob over the island. It was a magical place that island – flat and marshy, except for some higher ground in the middle, surrounded by bird-haunted mud-flats and saltings covered and uncovered by the restless tides.

We had lunch with the Eagles – good English roast lamb and mint sauce. It was all very emotional. We had loved living with the Eagles and helping them on their lovely farm. They had liked having us because we were a real farm family and Charlie said we were worth our weight in gold!

"I suppose you'll be sailing on the next tide," said Charlie. "We shall miss you together!"

Bob and I both spoke up at once for we had a single thought. What I said was: "We shall not be sailing on the next tide

Charlie! We shall stay here until you have found replacements for us to milk the cows and make the cheese and do all the other jobs."

"I misdoubt I won't find anybody to take your place together. Most of these so-called workers on the mainland aren't worth a light."

Well, Bob felt he had to get back to his little kingdom, or dictatorship, or whatever it was. Things were still ticklish there and he was afraid to leave it too long. He was right too. But the girls were wonderful. "There's three of us Ma," they said. "Who do you think you are? Do you think we can't milk a cow and make cheese? You go with Dad – we'll get along better without you!"

Thankless little beasts!

Anyways, Charlie Eagle said he knew of quite a good man at Lower Kirby who was willing to come and help him immediately and so it was decided that Bob and I should go back in *Suffolkman*, the girls should stay and help until replacements could be found, and the old *Suffolkman* would then come back for them: but at the last moment Charlie made them go with us.

Then Bob, Mick, the Eagles and I got down to talking business. The business was trade.

I like to think it was little me that partly persuaded Charlie to go in for a more intensive type of farming. Nature abhors a vacuum I told him. This island is seven hundred acres of good land. Start a little kingdom here. Get people over from the mainland – give them land – help them build houses – help them with their crops and stock. Make this a productive and fertile place. If you don't – one day they'll come over and take all you've got.

Anyways he decided to act on this advice. Or go part of the way along that road. So he wanted timber, for building material.

"We've got tons of pine," said Bob. "Corsican and Scots."

"Sawn?"

"Well – it might take a little time to get that organised."

"I could saw some up. I've got a circular rip-saw here and

Mick Miller has brought me quite a bit of diesel."

"Well it's up to us to provide milled timber in the end," said Bob. "And we will. John Hughes is already working on a water-driven band-saw. But meanwhile we can send you a barge-load of un-sawn timber."

"Well this island's very overstocked with sheep," said Charlie. "And we could let you have some in-calf heifers."

So it was arranged.

Charlie Eagle was on the Tendring Hundred Council and we all had a long talk about politics. The Council, apparently, was dead scared of the Midland army. So far Essex had kept the army out but it might not be able to do so for ever. Charlie was delighted to hear about the Fen Tigers and the other insurgents that were keeping the army busy. Bob said: "Send 'em arms. That's the one thing they lack."

Now I'm a pacifist – always was and always will be. I just hated all the fighting. I still think non-violence would have been more cost-effective. Complete non-violence and non-cooperation on the Ghandian model would have worked better in the end. When I heard Bob's story I kept thinking how easily the cat could have jumped the other way! Time and again the future of the rebellion hung by a hair – if the hair had broken the other side would have won. Bob would have been killed, the army would have triumphed and no doubt set up as nasty a little dictatorship as any since Adolf's. I still believe that consistent unwavering non-violence is the only force that will win the final battle.

But I guess I kept these sentiments to myself. I was so pleased to see dear old Bob and he was so pleased at the achievement of his guerrillas – or bandits or whatever you like to call them, that I certainly wasn't going to spoil his fun.

We were both worried about Robin, of course. It was the one big anxiety. "He's a tough little chap," said Bob, "but twelve's a bit young to go and be a bandit."

When we got back Charlie Eagle tried to persuade Bob to stay right there. "I'll give you a hundred acres of the island," he said.

"And stock it for you and help you get started. Real farmers are few and far between. We could get along well here together."

"I can't think of anywhere I'd rather live than this island," said Bob. "But, no, there are reasons why I've got to go home."

So Mick Miller sailed the *Suffolkman* into the little creek at the west of the island and we helped him sling thirty ewes, all Border Leicester-Cheviot half-breeds, thirty hoggetts and a ram, from the shore with a tackle from the end of his spreet and lowered them into his hold. Then down went four in-calf South Devon cows. Bob like the idea of Devons because he thought they would make good draught animals. We would keep the ewes for breeding of course but we decided to have a mass slaughter of the hoggetts and ration the meat out to people who were starved of the stuff.

All this was to be paid for in timber and salt herrings by and by.

Essex had no timber. Hardly any at all: the landscape was one great bulldozed agribusiness desert. One thing Essex did have though was guns. The old regular army had had a great arsenal at Colchester. Charlie, being a big cheese on Tendring Hundred Council, promised that he would put the suggestion to the Essex Federation that they should let us have some of these armaments in return for timber. The motivation behind this was not just that they needed timber. It was because they hated and feared the Midland army and thought that at any moment it would attack them. They had already had ultimata from General Wicklow to say that Essex must return to a united Great Britain which meant, of course, Wicklow's command. They had far more arms than they could use – if they gave us some and we used them well it would take the pressure off Essex. The Midland army had already made an abortive water-borne attempt to take Harwich.

In the end old Eagle found replacements for the girls so they, and Eli's wife, Mary, were able to come with us too.

When we had sailed south aboard *Suffolkman* I had been so damned miserable I hadn't noticed what was going on at all except that I was sea-sick. But to my dying day I will never forget that voyage back! Gee – it just blew my mind! I don't know how they could give such a prosaic name as barge to that magical ship! Overhead was this towering wall of red canvas – and when the wind took it it would lean right over against the sky and the huge great box it was driving would crash through the little waves. The heavy lee-boards – sort of side-keels that hung down each side of the hull and were as big as the side of a small barn – thundered against the sides, the great bluff bows would slap down on the water and when we "came about" the great spreet – a huge diagonal spar that held the mainsail and topsail out – came crashing across over our heads and the main-sheet block – as big as a baby – would come crashing across the wooden traveller.

My daughters had made several voyages in *Suffolkman* already – and boy were they superior! Oh yes, they knew it all, and kept on telling their ignorant old mother what it was all about.

I remember Bob and me sitting up on the forehatch – with the great red big-bellied foresail straining over our heads like a team of cart horses and Bob said: "If this is post-CRASH sea travel it's a change for the better!" And just then a great dollop of spray came over the bow and drenched the both of us!

Bob and Mick, who had always got on like blood brothers, struck a bargain. Bob would give Mick a cottage down on the estuary near Cragpit and give him help to set up a shipyard there. In return Mick would base his barge there and help establish a trade with other parts of the country.

"And the first thing I'll do is sail up to Colchester and load up a freight of arms," he said.

"Oh Mick – surely we've had enough bloodshed and killing?" I said.

But Bob was adamant. "I shan't rest until we've kicked those bastards right out of East Anglia," he said. "We shan't be safe until we do."

"Tell you what," said Mick. "We'll make Gretford a port again, like it was in the Middle Ages. We'll start ship-building again. We'll train sailors. We'll trade all up and down the coast and over the other side . . ."

"Mick – trade to Spain and bring back wine, olive oil, olives and oranges. And I'll love you for ever more."

"What could we take them they haven't got?" said Mick.

"Wool for a start," said Bob. "And cloth one day. And salt herring."

I was dozing in the warm fo'c'sle – there was a big coal-burning stove up there – when the roar of the anchor chain woke me up. I went on deck to find the barge anchored just off the mouth of the Gret. We had to stay there for several hours to wait for water to get over the bar. We then sailed in and sailed alongside Gretford Quay.

Willing helpers unloaded the animals. Bill Smithers took charge of them. The hoggetts were distributed to the butchers of the district to be killed and the meat to be distributed to the people who needed it most. The ewes and two cows were taken to Cragpit where they could be looked after.

As for the Hurlocks – we settled in to Cragpit Farm and it felt just as if we had never left it.

The army had looked after it. They had not been too bad. They had kept my plants going, thank God. Our six orphans, who had been with us before we were taken away, came back to live with us again and it was lovely to have them. I was so pleased to see they were pleased. We made 'em work – we all had to work – but we loved them and they loved us.

Oh gee, oh my – was it good to be home! The only dark shadow was Robin. But somehow, I never really lost hope about him. After all – what could happen to him? Who would kill a little boy after all? And there were no tigers in England.

Chapter Twenty

by Bob Hurlock

When the emotional storm had blown over we had breakfast: good home-cured ham and bacon, eggs, wholemeal bread and butter and coffee. They did well on that island. Having Mick Miller based there helped.

We then had to go out and help the farmer feed the stock and milk the cows. He milked twenty cows and made butter and cheese. Mary Woolpit was there, living-in with the farmer and his wife; and she was overjoyed to see me and hear news of Eli.

The farmer was a delightful man. He said that my family had been invaluable to him. "Real farm people," He said. "I've tried out townies from the mainland to help here but they're each worth two men short."

He excused Jessie and the children further duties that morning, and we sat in the cottage, by a coal fire (favour of the *Suffolkman*), and told each other our stories.

"What can have happened to Robin?" said Jessie.

"He'll be all right," I said. "He's a tough and resourceful boy. If he got up to the Brecklands – after all he could have done it quite quickly on a bicycle – either the army would have got him and put him in a home or somebody would have picked him up and looked after him. After all – there are no lions about."

"Wasn't that naughty though, running away like that? Surely he could have come back by now? Oh I do hope he's all right."

"Where do you suppose Hugh Giles went?" I asked.

"Well – the thing was – if he stayed on this island he would have to work. Naturally. And of course that was something Hugh had never experienced. You can imagine how he reacted to that suggestion. The last we saw of him he was heading for London."

"London? What did he expect to find there?"

"He said he wanted to find what was left of the old Carlton Hotel. For sentimental reasons. And off he went."

The farmer asked us all to lunch, and a good dinner it was too: roast mutton and mint sauce. It was the first really good meal I had had for a long time. It made me realise how well we might have lived at Gretford since the CRASH if the blessed army had not come in and looted all our food.

The farmer was on the Tendring Hundred Council, and an influential man.

"I'm delighted to hear you succeeded in defeating this blasted Midlands army," he said. "We've had set-tos with them, you know. They claim to be the official central government of England, which is complete nonsense of course. Our frontier is the Stour, and so far they have only tried to violate it twice. We have our own little army you see – regulars who were in this district at the CRASH. But I've always been afraid that, if this army did attack us, in the end they might win. They are numerically very strong, and very well armed. I expect it's largely due to your efforts that they haven't done it."

"And to the Fenmen," I said. I told him what I knew about them.

"Pity we can't get some arms to them," he said. "We have enormous dumps of arms and ammunition at Colchester. Far more than we need."

"If I could find a way of transporting them – would you let us have some arms?" I said. "After all, we would use them fighting your enemy. If we keep the Midlanders busy they're less likely to attack you."

"You could have as much as you liked. We don't want more than a certain amount – and we've got all we need. We're arming and training a Home Guard – but you know – we need every man-jack on the farm – we can't afford to mess about playing soldiers."

We talked about other possible trade, if we could persuade Mick Miller to help us. "We've got soft wood," I said. "Pines by the million. We've got about a score of deserters now, from the Midlanders, to cut them. You seem to have plenty of stock – sheep and cattle . . ."

"More than we want."

"I imagine so. Couldn't we work a trade?"

"My sheep will double next spring. We're overstocked with sheep and cattle in this part – I shan't be able to get rid of them. You get Mick to load up sheep when you leave – and we can spare a few cows too."

We arranged, then, that Mick should sail back with us, to the Mudde, with a load of cattle and sheep, and return in due course loaded with pines. There were no trees at all on the island, beyond a few big elms which it would be a crime to cut down. Coal was short and likely to become shorter. The Tendring Hundred itself was short of trees, and in any case the transport over to the island would be prohibitive. A barge load of pine would be worth its weight in gold to the farmer. "Also," he said. "I must build some more houses on this island. Somehow, I must get more people over. I say – what about you staying here? You can have the cottage. You can have a block of land of your own too."

"Well – it is a land of milk and honey," I said. I thought of war-torn Gretford District. I thought of the looming, impending blockading Midlanders. I thought of Gretford's own disgruntled middle classes. I thought of my wife and children. Why should they go back to all this? "I'll talk to Jessie about it."

After the washing up, and when Jessie and I had gone back to the cottage, I said to her: "What about staying here?"

"I'll go wherever you go, Bear."

"It's pretty grim back home," I said. "If you had seen the vicar and Lady Mary together digging twice-grown potatoes out of a field full of fat hen you'd know what I mean."

She thought for a while. Then: "You couldn't desert old Dike, Bear. And Eli – and the other chaps you hid in the forest with. You know you couldn't."

And when I thought about it, I knew that she was right. God knows my family was important to me, but I felt that I would, in a way of speaking, lose them, if I tried to gain them by deserting my friends.

Mick agreed to take us back in the barge, and we spent a day building a wire-netting kraal, or enclosure, on the top of an old barge wharf which was up a short creek on the north side of the island. The farmer had partially repaired this ancient wharf (perhaps when I was a small child sailing barges were going in there to load hay and straw for London). One high tide, Mick sailed his barge up the little creek, and tied up alongside the wharf. We drove a flock of sheep into the kraal that we had made and slung the sheep, one by one, up on a tackle from Mick's spirit-end and lowered them into the after-hold. In this way we loaded thirty ewes and a ram, and thirty hoggetts. I decided that we would kill the hoggetts as soon as we got home and have a mighty gorge in celebration.

In much the same manner we loaded four cows into the fore-hold: all Devons. I was delighted to get the Devons, because I thought they would make good draught cattle.

Watering these animals aboard was, of course, a big problem. We solved it partially by loading a quantity of mangolds which, of course, contain a lot of water. While we still lay in the creek we pumped fresh water aboard with a hand-pump from the delft, or dike behind the sea-well. But we knew that, as soon as we had cast off and sailed away, the animals would have no water, except that in mangolds, until we got home.

We were to leave the little yacht with the farmer for security. We would take possession of her again when Mick got back with his barge-load of wood.

The day came when the breeze was southerly, and the high tide at six p.m. We left at high-water, and Mick felt his way down the West Water in the growing dark. He wished to sail part of the south Suffolk coast in darkness – and well out to sea – to avoid a battle with any army boats that might come out to us.

I had never sailed in a barge before, and the experience was mind-blowing. The mighty mainsail and topsail blacked out the stars swung out by their enormous spar that Mick called the "spreet". Mick and his mate, and young Dickie, put me up to the names of these things. My daughters, too, bandied nautical terms about and gloried in one-upmanship over me. They had sailed in a barge. Diana and Jean had made one or two more trips with Mick since they had arrived at the island. And a bizarre note was struck, among all the nautical sounds, by the bleating of sheep and the lowing of cattle coming up from the holds while the heavy "lee boards" thundered against the wooden sides.

Jessie and I were sitting up on the fore-hatch covers, with the billowing foresail above our heads – straining at its ropes like a team of cart-horses – pulling that huge bulk of timber through the water. "If this is post-CRASH sea travel," I said, "it's a change for the better." Jessie agreed. Mick came up and joined us. He had handed over the Wheel to Dickie – to please the boy as much as anything I supposed.

I had heard Mick complaining that there was a lot of work to be done in the way of repairs to the hull of the barge.

I said to him: "Mick, if we could get your repairs done at Gretford – would you do something for us? Something, that is, more than you have already done which is a hell of a lot?"

"Well you know I'll do anything I can," he said. "I still feel bad that I couldn't rescue you when they took you off prisoner."

"When you sail back to the island with the load of pine – would you then go up the Colne to Colchester and load a really big load of arms and ammo?"

"Yes. Are you going to war again?"

"I want to kick those Midland bastards right out of Suffolk and Norfolk," I said.

"Yes – I'll do it. I was going to ask you something, Bob."

"Ask away."

"Could I base myself on the Gret?"

"Mick, if you base yourself on the Gret we will give you any house you like in the whole district – even if it means kicking some poor old widow-woman out. We will feed you on the fat of the land. What fat there is that is. We will give you all the labour you require to work on your barge. Whatever you want, if we can get it, you might have it."

"I'd only want a little old cottage. Somewhere near the water."

"But why do you want to? Wouldn't you be better off where you are – or at Brightlingsea for example?"

"Well – do you know – when the CRASH came, of course I was horrified and all that. Millions starved to death and the rest of it. Who wouldn't be? But then – I found shelter with you – and I liked what you were doing – dividing up the land like you did. You know – I always hated our old society. That's why I escaped from it – went to sea. Our society was rotten, too soft. Everyone was getting as soft as . . ."

"I know," said Jessie.

"Yes – well I hated it. Then I saw you – all good countrymen – trying to get on your own feet – live as people ought to live, in my opinion, and I like it, you know. I thought that – somehow – in spite of all that horror – the CRASH might have done some good. Then I saw that bloody army – parasites from the big cities. You know – you've read old Cobbett? He called London the Great Wen. That means a sore, I suppose. Well if it was a wen in his day – what was it in our day? And all these other huge cities – divorced from the land – completely cut off from the people who grow the food – crammed full of people who never worked at all, really, either with their hands or their brains. What were those cities but great Wens? Great cancers on the body of our countryside? And they burst. That's what happened – they just burst. And this army that came – it seemed to me like the pus out of them. This pus spread out and nearly poisoned the rest of the body. We did hear rumours, you know, that you'd kicked them out of your part – but they were only rumours. News doesn't travel between your part and Essex. But then, when you came along and told us how you'd beaten them, then I thought I'd like to come and live up there. Might do you a bit of good in one way or another."

"My dear Mick," I said. "You'd save us. We're blockaded, you know. You could bust this blockade. You'd make the difference between our surviving – and being overrun."

"Tell you what," said Mick. "We'll make Gretford a port again – like it was in the Middle Ages. We'll start ship-building there – out of wood."

"What do you do for sails, Mick?"

"Still plenty of canvas lying about. Old lorry covers – stack covers – stuff like that. It'll run out one day though."

"We want to start growing flax," I said. "We'll start a flax industry. Canvas – and rope. Hemp too, for rope, and linseed oil to oil your timbers!"

"Well fine. That's all for the future though. At the moment – we've got to concentrate on surviving – and kicking this army out. Clearing up the pus."

Mick went aft and took the wheel again. The rest of us went down below in the warm cabin, and dozed the night away. The roar of the anchor cable woke me up and I went on deck to find that Mick and his mate had anchored the barge just off the mouth of the Gret. We had to lay there to wait for sufficient water to get over the bar. By six o'clock we were tied up to Gretford Quay.

Willing people soon came to help us unload the animals. The cows were distributed out amongst smallholders who had no cows but could look after them. The ewes and the ram were handed over to Bill Smithers, Minister of Livestock. They would remain in his care until they had increased sufficiently, together with the rest of our sheep, for there to be enough to distribute. The hoggetts were distributed to the butchers in the District to slaughter, so that people could have some fresh meat for a change.

As for the Hurlocks, we settled in at Cragpit Farm, and you might have thought that we had never left it. Dickie Quantrill, refusing the offer of a holding of his own, settled in with us. He and Diana seemed to have a lot to say to each other. Jessie, with Dickie's help, and the help of the children and the half-dozen orphans who came back to us, ran the fifty-acre farm. Jessie also took over the job of salvaging her seed-growing garden again.

I set about organising the cutting of a barge-load of pine trees, and transporting the cut logs to our creek to load onto the barge. We dare not risk sending the *Suffolkman* up the River Gret; she would be at the mercy of the army there. We controlled the spit of shingle that separates the Gret from the sea, in its lower reaches, and so lying in the Gret down there she was safe. In a week she was loaded (we carried the logs down on old lorry chassis pulled by oxen) and was then ready for sea. She sailed away on the tide one night, with twenty armed men on board to guard her. She was our trump card. We were not going to risk her.

We settled down to the work of government again. The situation was still terribly difficult.

We had a very late spring that year. As you find if you live not only in but on the country, the late winter and early spring is the hungry gap. It is then that the shoe really pinches. Cattle and sheep have forgotten what grass tastes like; your hay is dangerously near running out, and if it does it is a disaster; your roots (mangolds, turnips and the like) are running out or going rotten in the clamp; you know it will be months before you taste a new potato and the old ones are finished; your cow is rapidly going dry; the pigeons have finished off the last of your winter and spring greens; you are so sick of eating parsnips that you would rather eat nothing. Pre-CRASH farming had ironed out this terrible seasonal valley in nutrition. Silage, cheap hay, large-scale root growing – to say nothing of hundreds of thousands of tons of animal feeding-stuffs imported from abroad – had kept the animals fed. Food came from the other side of the world for humans too.

But we, in that cold late spring of 20 - -, had no such aids, and life was very difficult indeed. Hungry people were having to work physically extremely hard preparing land which would life was very difficult indeed. Hungry people were having to work physically extremely hard preparing land which would produce food in six months' time. And the ground remained frozen far into March, and not a bud came out on the trees. The people of Gretford District had it tougher then than they had ever had it before.

I gathered together all the available bullocks (the army had left twenty young steers with London Farming) and broke them in to the yoke. To help me do this I had a team of army deserters. John Hughes set his boffins on to designing and building carts and wagons, using axles and wheels and tyres from the many redundant motor vehicles that lay about. In fact many a lorry got stripped down to form an ox wagon later on.

Transport was one of our worst problems. There was no way of carrying fire-wood from the forests in Gretford, for example, for a long time, but by hand-barrow. John Hughes' boys started a system of carrying logs to the Gret making rafts of them and letting the ebb tide take them down to Gretford. But at first everything, nearly, had to be humped by manpower. It was a long time before we had bred up and trained enough oxen to provide everybody with beasts of transport. As for horses: our mare had a female foal, which was fine, but then we could not get her in foal again because we did not have a stallion.

The worst thing for the morale of the people that winter though, was the dark. There was absolutely no oil for lamps. No candles. Not enough animal fat to make any. People got up before first light and started to grope around in the dark – so as to have as much daylight as possible – but in the middle of the winter this was not much. If you piled up a big fire in the evening – so that at least you could see something in your room – you had to go and get an awful lot of wood from the forest next day. One thing that happened: the art of conversation revived. Also of singing. People would sit around a fire in the evenings and have long sing-songs, with intervals of story-telling. It was the only thing they could do in the dark.

But the story-telling was not enough to stop people from

I was helping Jessie sow parsnip seed in the garden one cold morning, when a deputation came along. There was the Gretford vicar, the Reverend Bill Smythe; the son of an erstwhile rich farmer, named Jones (I always thought him as an arrogant young man – with nothing to be arrogant about); a retired general's wife (a terribly formidable woman); and a man who had been a very senior civil servant in days gone by and who had – by great good fortune for him – been visiting a sick relation in Gretford when the CRASH came. They were all the hard core of the old Conservative Party that we had beaten in the election.

I took them into our living room and told Jean to make them some tea. (We had a very small quantity of this commodity which Mick Miller had given us. I thought it would be a treat for them.)

"Tea!" said the general's wife.

"Yes – tea," I said.

They all sat down.

"Why we've come to see you," said the ex-civil servant, whose name was Bryant, "is that we think it's time we had an election."

"Well when we had the last one," I said, "we didn't specify any period before which we should have another one. But I think four years . . ."

"We do not think that the last election still holds valid," said the parson. "You see – there has been a complete change of government since then. And – after all – when we had the last election we did not know that there was in fact an already established legal government of the whole country . . ."

"You don't mean the army?" I said.

"Well yes – they are commanded by an officer who holds the sovereign's commission . . ."

"But there's another officer who holds the sovereign's commission in the North. They say he's senior in rank to this one. What about his army being the legal government in the country? Also – by what legal argument do you make out that the army should be the government of the country anyway? Surely it's an English tradition that the army should always be under the civil power . . ."

"Yes but when the civil power is simply removed from the scene . . ."

"Well I tell you what," I said. "It's obvious that it's no good talking about legal positions. There aren't any anymore. I head the government here because my men and I have taken power by force. Put it that way."

There was silence for a short while: then the general's wife said: "Well – it's honest of you to admit it, anyway."

"But," said young Jones, who talked as though he had a plum in his mouth, "if you aren't afraid that you might get chucked out – why not hold an election? It would make your position much stronger."

"You'd be surprised how strong my position is already," I said. "But the reason why I won't allow an election is – I think I might lose it."

"You are just an out and out dictator then?" said the general's wife.

"I suppose I am," I said.

"What makes you think you would lose?" said the vicar. "You won before – hands down?"

"I think I might lose because the army still has some oil. You are all fed up with sitting in the dark. So am I. You are fed up with digging, and carrying things in wheel barrows. So am I. You hate the prospect of years of being nothing but peasants – tied to the soil – earning your bread in the sweat of your brow. You think if you got power again you would talk to the army. In return for some concessions – give back their deserters for one . . ." ("No, no!" said the vicar.) "Yes, yes," I said. "For if you didn't return them the army would come and get them. For certain concessions they would allow you a little oil. You would be able to light your lamps again. You might even hear the tractors humming. Those lovely tractors again. But if you did all this – the army would be in here again, boots and all. You couldn't stop them. You wouldn't want to very much."

"The army may have appeared very terrible to you," said the vicar. "They took your farm – arrested you and all that. But that was that bad man Clifford Brown's doing. And that terrible weak fellow Major Dobson let him do it. I don't know what it was – Brown seemed to have complete power over Dobson. But that was all unusual. The army wasn't very terrible in other ways."

"They took our grain, or nearly all of it, and nearly all our stock. It's through them that we're hungry now."

"They were only so hard on us because of you people in the forest. They were fighting a war."

"You would let the army in again," I said, "for a miserable little bit of oil. The spring will come one day 'though God knows when'. When it does come the days will get longer – the grass will grow – there'll be some milk for the children – we'll even get some green vegetables again one day. By next winter, mark my words, the army won't have any oil. Nobody will. Even you, I fancy, have given up the belief that oil is going to come from America. It isn't. We're going forward – sooner or later, to a wind, horse and ox civilisation. With maybe a little coal-fired steam. I am not going to see our transition to this civilisation put back another year or two just for the price of a few months more of oil. I'm going to stay in power until we have made this transition."

Jessie and the girls came in, we had some tea, everybody was very polite, and then they went away.

I knew, though, that my position was not as strong as I made out to these people.

For you cannot have a dictatorship in an armed community.

By issuing arms out to two hundred members of the Home Guard – arms which individual citizens kept in their houses and treated as their own – government by force, against the will of the armed majority, was impossible. True – we had been selective in issuing the weapons. I wouldn't have given an automatic to young Jones, for example. Our salvation lay in the fact that most of the weapons were held by people who had taken over smallholdings, and they had had their holdings long enough, and worked at them hard enough, for the land to mean something to them. They would fight to retain it. And they would endure a

little hunger, and hard work, and darkness. For the first time in
their lives they were not just landless refugees in their own
country: confined to the public roads and parks. England really
had become "their" land.

Even so, hunger and discontent became very strong that
hungry-gap. And I think there might have been trouble, had not
the *Suffolkman* returned from her voyage with not only a huge
load of arms and ammunition – about a hundred tons of it – but
also a lot of other things. For Mick, the marvellous chap, had
arrived at the mouth of the Colne to be told by the Tendring
Hundred government that they would certainly give him the arms
(as the Horsey Island farmer had promised me) but that it would
take them a week or two to sort them out. Now Mick had
collected, in his previous trading, a large amount of Tendring
Hundred currency. With this he bought a flock of sheep, which
he had loaded, on Mersea Island, and carried up the London
River. He had been able to trade them there for a large quantity
of goods: such things as paraffin oil, candles, oil lamps, tools,
tea and coffee, bolts of cloth, clothes of all sorts, and other odds
and ends too numerous to mention. Returning to the Colne he
had loaded the arms, and here he was back in the Gret.

There was great rejoicing. The goods were divided out – sold
through the shops – and I saw to it that everybody got something.
Lamps were lit again – people tasted the solace of tea –
everybody became more cheerful.

While I was attending to all this, and wondering what to do
with a hundred tons of arms and ammunition including a twenty-
five pounder gun and a hundred shells for it – I got word, in my
office, that Eli had come back.

A young fellow came across the square to tell me. He said
he was in *The King's Head*. "And there's somebody with him,"
he said.

"Anyone I know?" I asked.

"You ought to know him – he's your son."

Chapter Twenty-One

by Bob Hurlock

"Robin," said Diana, after Robin had been back in the bosom of his family for a few hours. "You may have been a bandit among the yellowbellies, as you call them. You may have shot chups, as you call them, through the goots, as you call them, but you are not among yellowbellies now. You are back in Suffolk, and you'll either talk good Suffolk or else standard English."

Robin had come home, after his year in the bush, with an almost opaque Lincolnshire accent. He told us, of course, his story. Indeed, if we hadn't suppressed him, he would have told it to us many times. He had cycled happily away to the Brecklands, to look for me in my prison camp. After sundry adventures he had fallen in with a gang of Fen Tigers. They had taken him in on the strength that he was a sort of mascot. It had always been their intention to attack the prison camp at Wretham and release the prisoners, but they had not been able to do so until indeed the camp was closed and the prisoners transferred to Nottinghamshire. Robin had hung in with the gang, because they had left Norfolk and gone across the Fens to the Lincolnshire Wolds. Thus, he had never had news that I was free and operating back in the woods at home. Then, on coming back to the Brecklands for a spell, he had, by chance, fallen in with Eli. And Eli had brought him home. Eli just couldn't wait to get to his little wife, and that evening they both went to *The Barge* and went to *The Barge* and she gave him a black eye.

Now when the *Suffolkman* sailed in to the Gret with her hundred tons of armaments I was immediately under very strong pressure from our "war party" (led by Eli and John Lloyd) to launch a frontal attack at Willingham Castle immediately. We were all tired of being blockaded. The spring had come – people were not so hard-pressed – and many men were anxious to attack the enemy and settle the issue once and for all.

Both Dike and I had other ideas however. We did not want to see a lot of people killed. Particularly we did not want the place overburdened with wounded men. "There are more ways," said Dike, at a council meeting, "of killing a cat besides strangling it to dead."

John Lloyd – and his father Sir Charles – were both doing propaganda for immediate attack. Young John was the most active. I could see that I was going to have trouble with him. All he wanted to do was to go and shoot some more enemy with his father's elephant rifle. And several other young men could not bear to see that hundred tons of hardware lying idle in Gretford while our enemies were all about us. I felt sure myself that there was a better plan than a frontal attack, but I needed a little time to find what it was. I felt that we should wait. But people became more and more impatient.

It was Mick Miller who thought of a plan, and outlined it to a meeting of our inner council: Dike, Eli and myself.

"Look here," he said. "Let me load up half those arms in the barge. I'll sail round to the Wash – go up the Nene-Wisbech River. Deliver the arms to this mad doctor fellow. He'll dish them out to his Fen Tigers or whatever he calls them. They'll do our fighting for us. We won't have to fire a shot".

The strategy of this was so obviously sound that there could be no argument. With the Fenmen really on the offensive the enemy's forces in East Anglia would be completely cut-off. We sent for young John Lloyd – who even at that moment was over in *The King's Head* holding forth to anyone who would listen that I had lost my nerve, and wouldn't attack the enemy until the enemy attacked us and then it would be too late.

In he came, looking sullen, like a boy brought before the headmaster for bolshiness.

"John," I said. "You terrible boy. Here are your orders. You will take your elephant rifle, twenty chosen volunteers, and fifty tons of arms and ammunition. Enough for an army. You will go aboard Mick's barge and sail to the Wash. You will hand the arms over to Doctor Jenkins and his merry men – and you will go ashore yourself and place yourself and ten of your men under his command. When the war is over, which it will be very soon, I hope, you will make your way back overland to here. Mick will bring the barge back as soon as you are unloaded and the wind serves. Any questions?"

John was pleased as a puppy-dog with ten tails. And shortly the *Suffolkman* was furnished forth.

Her wheel-house was protected by sand-bags from small arms fire. Two big tanks were bolted to her deck to carry water. The Gretford village baker made ship's biscuits. Sheep were killed and put down in salt and more were penned up in the bow for live rations. The butcher from Muddebridge, a great pigeon fancier, came up with a crate of racing pigeons: to be used for communication.

And at dead of night the *Suffolkman* sailed: with John and his twenty men and Mick and his permanent crew.

I have no doubt that it was this voyage of the sailing barge that brought an end to the rule of the army, not only in East Anglia, but in England.

The pigeons came back, one by one, and each brought good news. The first one told us that the barge had reached Sutton Bridge, in the mouth of the Nene, and that Mick had contacted an old friend of his named Lineham who was a fisherman there. (There was something in the message about a "monumental booze-up"!). The second, several days later, said that the barge was at Wisbech and the arms were being unloaded. "Yellowbellies delighted". The next came from the *Suffolkman*, at sea off Cromer, sailing home with some horses for us. The fourth pigeon, which had been taken ashore with "Lloyd-force", arrived with the news that the Fenmen intended to launch an offensive in early May. That cheeky boy John had added a footnote: "Eat the pigeon."

And the next thing we knew was that when we looked out of the window one morning we saw the *Suffolkman* lying at anchor in the Gret. We found she had aboard her a Suffolk stallion and two Percheron mares: gifts of the Fenmen, and, if they had ransacked the world, they could not have thought of anything better to send us.

We waited until the first week in May, and then began guerrilla activity against the enemy. We had sailed, in small yachts, small quantities of arms to other groups of people along the coast, and we sent word to these to step up activities. We wished to help the Fenmen as much as we could by pinning down the enemy.

In the second week in May some of our men came back across the Gret, with the news that a large motorised column of the enemy had left Willingham, bound westwards. They were not sure how many but judged that there must be several hundreds. The enemy had been very wary of using oil for a long time; this, then, was the using of closely-guarded reserves. They were obviously off to help their companions against the Fenmen.

It was then that we began to press home our final attack.

Dike led a large force, with the twenty-five pounder gun, across the neck of land between the Mudde and the Gret. Keeping to the strip of woodland in there, it was possible for the gun to be got within comfortable range of Willingham. An artillery officer, who had deserted from the army and who had a score to settle with it, was in charge of the gun. Our main force was kept in reserve around the gun: both to protect it and its line of supply, and to be ready for a frontal attack.

A strong force, all on bicycles, under Eli Woolpit, set off round the south of Willingham, with the intention of cutting off the enemy from that direction and also from the rear.

A third force, of about seventy men, pushed bicycles heavily-laden with mortars and bombs round to the north of Willingham.

Their role was to create a diversion on that flank, while the main attack went in frontally.

This third force nearly came to grief. They got to within mortar range of the castle in the darkness, without being discovered, and then started to dig themselves in on the side of a hill. The enemy came out at daybreak with what must have been most of his force: perhaps a hundred men and two armoured cars. There was a bazooka with the screen of our men which had been put out in front of the mortar base-plate position, but the man who operated it lost his nerve. He fired away a dozen rockets without scoring one hit, and then ran away. The enemy armoured cars came on, with the infantry, supported by heavy fire from positions near the castle. Our men in front of the mortars were too harassed by the covering fire from the direction of the castle to fire their own weapons effectively, and it looked as if they, too, must be over-run. They were saved by No. 1 on one of the mortars: a deserter from the army named Sergeant Smith. When the enemy were running up the hill not a hundred yards away from him he began to remove all the bags of cordite from the tails of his bombs, leaving only the primers, thus giving them a range of only about fifty yards or less, and then he began to drop bombs just in front of his own position – right among the charging enemy. The effect was dramatic. The enemy at once got down – many of them killed or wounded – and never pressed home their attack. With leisure now to range their weapons, the four mortar crews began to put bombs down on the enemies' covering-fire positions, and that, together with a few well-placed smoke bombs, enabled our riflemen to get their heads up long enough to pour fire down on to the enemy who were pinned down on the slope. These were forced to flee, leaving many dead. The armoured cars had been held up by a stream. One was knocked out by a very brave man who ran forward and picked up the bazooka from where it lay in front of its dead No. 2 – and the other car turned and lumbered away. Certainly this was the turn of the battle, and, indeed the whole war.

The artillery officer in charge of our twenty-five pounder

managed to establish a very good operating position and was soon sending shells screaming over in well-directed and highly selective fire. Dike moved up with his main attacking force, but never had to attack. The white flags broke out over the castle. The defeat that morning, and the un-expectedness of the shelling, had shattered their morale.

The enemy wanted to march out with their arms. Dike said no: they could march out and go back to the Midlands but they could take nothing with them beyond clothes. They were not in a position to argue. We found later that there were only two hundred of them there, mostly not front-line troops anyway, and they had been completely unprepared for a massive attack with mortars and artillery. They surrendered unconditionally.

Willingham was full of frightened girls. I don't think, actually, that many of them had been taken there, as they claimed, by force. We gave the girls the choice of going away with their fallen heroes, or else coming to us and working a longish passage to full citizenship.

And that was the end of the war.

We got a very satisfactory amount of loot, of course. The best of it were the horses. The army, at last realising, I suppose, that the oil really was coming to an end, had started to gather together horses: mostly either hunters or else children's ponies, but nevertheless horse-flesh, capable of being worked, and some of them of breeding. True, half of them we later had to return to their rightful owners. But we still kept a dozen, and they went a long way towards solving perhaps our most intransigent problem of all: transport. There was a nice bit of paraffin stored away in Willingham, and as for such items as candles, lamps, wines and spirits, olive oil and other groceries, tools of all sorts, agricultural implements: the army had had the looting of most of East Anglia for a long time. It was all there. We decided to leave it there for the timebeing: to use Willingham as our central store, as it were. We realised that we could not hog all this stuff for Gretford district; it had got to be distributed out among all the East Anglian survivors.

And it was thus that the East Anglian Federation had its beginning.

Word was sent out north and south along the coast that there was to be a share-out of loot: or rather a returning of loot to its rightful owners. People came from the Stour to the Waveney. They came on bicycles, and naturally could take little back with them; but we arranged that what was theirs should be stored for them at Willingham, and they could draw it later as they liked. It was obvious that they would have, in the end, to move the heavier stuff by water. It would have to be carried overland to Randersfield and shipped by barge. Before these people went home we fixed a date for a great conference: a conference of people from all over East Anglia. The purpose of the conference was to set up an East Anglian Federation.

Nowhere in East Anglia had there grown up a local government as highly developed as ours at Gretford, and all the people who came from other pockets of life up and down the coast, and from new settlements inland, paid great attention to the kind of government we had set up, and the way we had divided the land and tried to set up industries, and they went home determined to copy us.

After most of them had gone we had a pleasant surprise.

John Lloyd turned up, with five survivors, from his expedition to the Fenlands. With him were my two old friends with whom I had been imprisoned: Michael Self, the Fenland engineer, and Tony Larkin.

The Fenmen, with their new arms, had been immediately and completely successful. They had imposed terms on the enemy providing that he withdraw completely from Northamptonshire, Rutland, Lincolnshire, and all places east. The counties immediately to the west of the Great Level were in the process of making a Federation similar to the one we hoped to set up in East Anglia.

The war was over, and we could set about re-building our shattered world.

Chapter Twenty-Two

by Ex-Lieutenant-Colonel John Nightingale

I know the quotation had been used before in this book but I must use it again: *Whom the Gods wish to destroy they first make mad!*

There in my academic headquarters in Cambridge, after the signal defeat of my command at Willingham, I was becoming more and more disturbed and uncertain about the whole business I was engaged in. Commanding English troops, I was fighting Englishmen. I had a suspicion that the Englishmen I was fighting I should have liked better than the ones I was fighting with. And they were beating me! As my command got larger and larger (I ended up with the numerical equivalent of two divisions) the quality of its men got lower and lower. I was having to commission men I certainly would not have bought a second-hand car from. The orders I was getting from above seemed madder and madder. I was to have women shot. If a woman's husband escaped from prison camp, the woman was to be shot. Now this whole question of whether a soldier should obey his conscience or his superior officer is a very difficult one, but it did not take me ten seconds to make up my mind on this.

No woman was to be shot, for any reason or under any circumstance, by my command, if I had anything to do with it. But, I have to admit, people continued to escape in large numbers from our prison camps and we just did not seem to be able to stop them.

But why, I thought, should there be prison camps at all? Surely we were dealing with Englishmen? These were not some foreign enemy. I just could not understand what was happening. I lay awake night after night trying to think it out to its conclusion. I began to realise that there was something wrong with our basic policy.

We were turning into so many looters! Our attempts to revive big industry were all failures. The cause was hopeless: we gave it up. Our attempts to increase production on the land failed completely. Without agricultural chemicals the big business farms were helpless. All we could do in fact was loot. We looted the country to feed the city. That was all.

At first, when we could billet men on each and every farm, this looting was easy. But when the insurgence started up we could no longer do this. Gangs of insurgents simply moved about the country wiping out our billetees. We had to withdraw them. My soldiers could no longer go about in anything less than platoon strength and everything had to be guarded. We became stretched to the limit.

We continually lost men but when the High Command wrote a peremptory letter to me asking "What was our body count"; I did not know what to reply. There was no body count. Our enemy were like ghosts – they struck – and vanished.

And then came this summons to go to Birmingham for a top-secret conference.

Whom the Gods wish to destroy they first make mad.

Sir Charles Wicklow, and the puppet civilian government he had set up of Birmingham businessmen, had decided to invade Wales.

Wicklow invited me to lunch, alone, before the conference

"I know you don't agree with this action," he said, over the port. "But we're being driven into it, John. Our hand is forced. And you must understand – we have right on our side. Wales is part of England – well, I mean, it's part of Great Britain which is the same thing – and so is Scotland. It is entirely right and just that we should re-unite the whole Kingdom and I will not rest until we have done so. Then we are going to invite the King back from Scotland."

"You realise we are fully stretched in England as it is," I said. "What possible thing can you hope to gain from attacking Wales? The Welsh are doing us no harm whatsoever and you said yourself that they seem far better off materially than we are."

"That's partly the trouble, John," he said. "You see – the border counties want to join them. We have already lost all the parts of England west of the Severn. You think you are having difficulties in East Anglia – it's nothing to what is happening in Shropshire, Herefordshire and Gloucestershire. They strike – and skip back over the border into Wales and there is nothing we can do about them."

"Let them go then – let them manage their own affairs."

"John, sometimes I don't quite understand you. I question sometimes whether you ought to be a soldier."

"What will you gain by this war?"

"Well perhaps you don't realise quite what's involved. You see, firstly, it will be a very short war. Our best appreciation of the situation puts the probable duration at not much more than a month."

"Why?"

"Well, although elements of the Welsh Command defected they have very few arms, no oil, and practically no ammunition. We have helicopters. You tried them over your pine forests and they didn't work. They will work over the bare Welsh hills. We have napalm . . ."

"Do you mean to tell me . . ." I started. I could hardly believe my ears.

"Why not? War's war. If you'd have used a little napalm on those pine forests you'd have roasted those damned bandits! You're too squeamish to be a soldier John. Now there's another thing – we need meat."

"Meat? We've been sending you thousands of head of cattle."

"But it's finished, John. You know dam' well it is. There's plenty of meat in the Pennines, but we haven't managed to reduce the north yet. We'll turn our attention to them the moment we've cooked the Welsh goose. We are out of meat. And the Welsh hills are covered from one end to the other with sheep. This is a matter of saving civilisation, John – don't you see? Do we want our British civilisation to survive – and return to normal – or not? You don't see all the factors as we do up here, and I can tell you we've got to crack this Welsh nut – we've got to re-unite this country under one government."

"Can I be relieved of my command, Sir?"

"What – you want a base job?"

"I would rather not have a job at all. I would like to resign my commission."

"What the hell would you do? You would starve. I don't hold anything against you, John, we were at Sandhurst together and all that. I will give you a cosy little sinecure up here, where we can keep an eye on you. I've been toying with the idea of replacing you for sometime. You're not pacifying East Anglia – you are far too soft. I'll send somebody down there who will fight with the gloves off. He'll have to because we shall need nearly the whole of your army for the Welsh job. One quick push, John – and Wales will be back in the British Empire again. I doubt if there'll be much fighting at all."

I was spared going to the conference. And in case this book is to be read by people of future generations who did not know what happened to the Welsh invasion I might as well tell it quickly here.

The Welsh had plenty of arms and ammunition after all. Their small regular army had the support of all the people. Wicklow's vaunted helicopters were all shot down within a week by a terrible instrument called the "blowpipe" which any infantryman could use. What was left of Wicklow's army had to swim back across the Severn and the Dee leaving everything they possessed behind them, their filthy napalm bombs and all. The Welsh, who seemed to have a very well-organised and effective civilian government, took over all the land west of both the Dee and Severn, to the delight of the inhabitants. And rumour has it that

the next communication that the Midland Command received
from the Welsh government was a challenge to a rugby match at
Cardiff Arms Park.

But back to my wretched affairs.

I went back to Cambridge with orders to send in at least three-
quarters of my army immediately to the Welsh border and then
await my replacement by another officer. The replacement might
not come for some time because all competent officers were to be
needed for the Welsh campaign.

I got back to Cambridge and began to find out what had
happened in my absence. My chief-of-staff reported to me: "That
old friend of yours – Hugh Giles? Fellow such a terror for the
women? We've got 'im. In the bag."

"What do you mean?"

"Didn't you know? He deserted. In a sailing barge! Southern
Command picked him up and sent him back here. He's awaiting
court-martial."

"Send him to me at once, will you."

Hugh duly arrived, with an officer of equal rank as escort.

I told the escort to go away.

"Have a whisky, old boy," I said.

"Can I believe my ears?" said Hugh. "I'll have to pinch my
bloody self to see if I'm awake."

He was his amusing old self. Still swearing and bombasting and
not the slightest bit abashed that he was under close arrest and
almost certainly going to be shot. We only had one punishment
for desertion by then.

We had a long talk, and finished the bottle of whisky.

He told me of things that had been going on in my command
that I knew nothing about. He told me how the trouble started in
Gretford District – the trouble that laid the foundations of our
defeat for there were fired the first shots of the war. He told me
of the rape and pillage that had been going on in my command.
Very little of this had ever leaked back to me. I felt ashamed of
what I had been in command of.

"Well," said Hughie after a time. "I suppose I shall face the firing squad. I hope you'll chose better shots than most of these city bastards your army is composed of. Most of 'em couldn't hit a barn door at five yards."

I sent for my staff car. I sent for my second-in-command. "Bill," I told him. "Our orders are to move the whole bloody army to Wales. Old Wicklow is going to invade it. How's that for a piece of news? So off you go – inform all units. Detailed orders will be here tomorrow or the next day. I'm off today – got an urgent appointment. I'm going to go and parley with some of those guerrillas and see if I can't get a gentleman's agreement with them to keep quiet while we're away. Don't tell a soul – it's top secret. Hugh Giles has turned King's evidence and is taking me to their secret lair."

Well, Hughie and I had four cases of whisky loaded in the back of my staff car and away we drove. I was delighted to see the sentry at King's College gate present arms like a real regular. I gave him a last salute. I was no longer a soldier.

In some forgotten part of Suffolk we broke down. Neither Hugh nor I were any good with engines. While we were wondering what the hell to do along comes this tribe of Gypsies. A young man, who told us his name was Bill Smith but whom we afterwards found out was really called Bert Herron, poked his head under our bonnet and had the car working in a couple of hours.

By then the caravan had moved on and so we gave Bert a lift along the road. There we found them, four old lorry chassis pulled by horses, a dozen grown-ups and countless children, and they asked us to have some tea.

Hughie immediately made friends with them. He admired their lurcher dogs, obviously knew what he was talking about, pretended to try to buy a horse, swore and cursed and ranted, the children crawled all over him and immediately took to him and their parents liked him too.

I could see that his swashbuckling, aristocratic, cavalier attitude appealed to these people. At heart he was one of them.

The upshot of it was that Bert Herron decided to come along

with us in the car. The others would follow with the grais and vardos as they called their transport, and join us later. Where? Well at Gretford, for that is where we were heading. To Bob's farm.

So I've reached the end of my story. Jessie and Bob shook hands with me, made me welcome with such warmth as I shall never forget, and took me on as one of their workers, to serve a three years' apprenticeship in farming. Then I shall get a farm of my own. It was hard at first – but they broke me in lightly. Now I'm as fit as a fiddle and as tough as an oak. I feel I am working my way back to true sanity – to a sane and healthy world where all have to work and all can enjoy the fruits of their labours. I am happier than I have ever been.

Bert Herron lives in a cottage at Bebbage with his beautiful little Gypsy wife. He has a huge and terribly untidy scrapyard and does a marvellous job converting old cars and lorries into horse-and ox-drawn vehicles.

As for Hugh Giles? Well it transpired that during his stay at Cragpit Farm he had stashed away a prodigious quantity of durable and very valuable goods in an old Royal Observer Corps bomb-proof shelter along the marshes. God knows how he had contrived to do this without anyone finding out, but he had done it. Bob, who was more or less king of the place during that time, allowed him to retain this stuff, and swap it firstly for the ruins of the old *Crown Hotel* and then for material and labour to repair the building and get it working as a pub again. And Giles is now the jovial landlord, although he does not actually do any work himself. Unless duck fighting and gun punting and hare coursing and being gallant with ladies and such like activities can be called work. But he is a roaring success as a landlord and *The Crown* has undoubtedly become the hub and social centre of Gretford District.

And that is my story: honestly told.

Chapter Twenty-Three

by Bob Hurlock

Michael Self and Tony Larkin came and stayed with us at Cragpit. They were there a fortnight, and we spent much of the time talking. The war was finally over; we all felt that we had to draw breath, stand back, try to see the wood for the trees.

I remember sitting in the garden one warm evening in June: Larkin; John Hughes, our Marxist Minister of Industry; Michael Self; Jessie and myself. We were sipping some very good cowslip wine. Home-made wine can be appalling – it can be superb. The birds were singing, there was a gentle breeze from the south-east, everything was peaceful.

"A thing that strikes me every so often nowadays," said Jessie, "is the silence. Except for birdsong now there is no noise. If you can remember – in the old days, there was hardly ever a moment without, somewhere, the noise of a jet engine, or a motor car, or a motor bicycle. Now you hear nothing but bird-song, the wind in the trees, sheep bleating, cattle lowing, people talking. I like it much better."

"I liked to hear the engines," said John Hughes. "This is the silence of stagnation. I shall be happy when the cars are buzzing along the roads again, and the aeroplanes humming."

"Do you think they ever will be?" said Jessie.

"Of course. Progress will start again."

"Progress to what?" she said. "There are so many different kinds of progress. Progress in so many different directions."

"There is only one direction," said Hughes. "Progress to greater and greater control over nature. Which is another way of saying – more and more mechanisation."

"You are utterly and completely wrong," said Larkin.

"Give reasons!"

"Your kind of progress was like the progress of the dinosaurs. It led up a blind alley. It was doomed to extinction. That alley – that clanking, petrol-stinking, mechanical alley of yours has been explored now by the Life-force and abandoned. We are back again at the cross-roads – and we must find another road; and let's hope it'll be the right one this time. Your alley came to an end the other day – at the Battle of Willingham."

"You mean we are now to sink back for ever into a miserable peasant existence?"

"Your petrol-stinking civilisation," said Larkin, "depended upon the majority of mankind living completely and utterly divorced from the soil. Man is the child of the Earth. We must live close to the Earth and in harmony with it. We are part of Nature. If he is divorced from it – taken to live in huge areas of sooty brick and tarmacadam – he goes wrong. He turns sour and unhappy. He loses his sense of the meaning of life. The sources of his strength and happiness have been cut off; his spiritual roots have been severed."

"Do you mean men can never live in towns again?"

"No, I don't mean that. But this time we must ensure – if we don't want to go the way we have gone again – that the towns are always part of the countryside. That is what is important. That the towns should be an organic part of the countryside around them. A town like Willingham was – and will be again. A town like London wasn't. It was completely and utterly divorced from its countryside. London's countryside was in the Argentine – in Australia. That was what was wrong."

"We must achieve the state in which the town and its surrounding country are interdependent, complementary, and existing for one another," he continued. "If we get to a culture nearly approaching the culture that the Greeks achieved in their city-states – how many thousand years ago? – we will have got somewhere."

"Slaves?" said Hughes.

"No. Free and independent people, not requiring slaves – or inhuman machines which completely dominate their lives – because they can live simply, and with few possessions. People dependent on the soil – and man must always be dependent on the soil or reach disaster – but people independent because each man has his own land, people living in fruitful co-operation with each other."

"But your people with few possessions: how poor they will be. No music – no drama – no literature – no art. Not that these things have ever meant much to me I admit – but you were saying the other day they were important to you."

"When was our best music composed?" Larkin asked. "Before the invention of the wireless and the gramophone – or after it? When was our best painting – our best sculpture done? Our best literature? Did Shakespeare have a typewriter? Did Beethoven have a hi-fi? Did Michaelangelo have a pneumatic pick? Do you know – it's frightful to contemplate – but I don't believe a jot of the art, literature, music or all the rest of it that was produced in the world in the last fifty years will survive. But Beethoven will survive. Mozart will survive. Shakespeare, Homer and Fielding, Swift, Boswell – a thousand others who worked in the pre-industrial world will survive. No. Mankind had taken a wrong turning. The true artist doesn't need jukeboxes, hi-fi equipment, ferro concrete, massive apparatus and machinery to make his art."

"No – but in your merry Mozart days how many people had this music? Mozart may have been a dam' fine musician – I wouldn't know – but his music was heard by a tiny circle. It wasn't until our day that the masses heard it."

"And what was the result? Before the "masses" as you call them came into existence – yes there were no masses before the industrial revolution – there were individual men and women. Before the day of the masses – men and women had their own music. Every country in Europe had a vigorous, lively, changing, folk music, folk art. It was from the good earth of this folk art that the great sophisticated flowerings of the Mozarts and Beethovens grew up. But the sickly flood of ersatz music and art which flooded out from your industrial conurbations withered and killed the folk art. And because the folk roots were killed sophisticated art became sterile and worthless. How much of the poetry that was written in the last fifty years will survive a decade? It was intellectual, sterile, clever rubbish."

"Well," said Jessie. "I don't think it's much good arguing whether industrial civilisation was good or bad – it is gone. I don't think, myself, men will ever have the heart to build the Birminghams and Wigans again – whether they were good or bad. But this I do believe and I've been meaning to speak up about it, only people could think of nothing while that horrible war was going on. We must not sink into mental and spiritual lethargy. We don't need to – and we mustn't. It is a fine thing to be a peasant . . ."

"Peasants are barbarians . . ." said Hughes.

"No," said Jessie. "Peasants are never barbarians. If there is an opposite to the word barbarian – it is the word peasant. We must be peasants. But there is no reason why we should not be an intellectually lively, spiritually alive peasantry."

Hughes said: "Morris dancing on the village green?"

"And why the hell not?" said Jessie. "Right on! If we go back to where we left off – pick up our real regional roots again from where they were cut off by cosmopolitanism and industrialism – maybe we will have something to build on. Develop an art – a culture – which is regional – which really stems from the soil of its own country. After all, you talk of all your wonderful music and art which was available to all the people before the CRASH. But was it really available? What did they really turn their television sets on to look at? What music did you hear coming out of the loud speakers? Rubbish from my bloody country, or worse rubbish imitated in England from America. Did they flood to the galleries to look at the pictures of Michaelangelo? Did they hell. They had no culture. The tunes they hummed were all bad and foreign – and they didn't last five minutes. They had no songs of their own."

"I've heard some dam' good songs in *The Barge*," I said.

"Ah yes. But they were songs left over from the time before the industrial music was emptied over us like so much slops."

"Well what do you suggest we do, Jessie?" I said. "To encourage a new art."

"We must go consciously out for it," said she. "We must make sure the most important thing is taught in schools – the making of art. The creation of it. Teach children to sing, to play instruments, to make instruments, to paint, to weave, to pot, to sculpt, to carve, to make up songs, to compose poetry. These things must be the basis of our education. These are the activities that make for happiness, for integrated people, for true culture as opposed to imposed culture."

"By God I agree!" exclaimed Larkin. "Before the CRASH our schools turned out a flood of barbarous, mechanically-minded apes – their heads stuffed with miserable figures and facts, their fingers skilled at nothing but pressing buttons, pushing pens in offices, and itching to get on the trigger of the nearest atom bomb rocket. They were the people you beat up at Willingham Castle, thank God."

"But you'll all starve in your Morris-dancing paradise!" said Hughes. "Surely the first thing to teach people is to control nature – to survive – the technical things. They're the things that enable us to live in a hostile universe. To help us conquer nature."

"Your conception of a hostile universe is the typical technocrat – big city – conception." said Larkin. "The universe is not hostile. We are designed – modelled by natural selection – to live and be happy in this very universe. People will soon learn to live with Mother Earth again – because we were designed to! It doesn't take long to milk a cow night and morning – and a cow gives enough milk for a lot of people. It doesn't take long to plough up an acre, and an acre grows an awful lot of wheat or potatoes. Let us henceforth live simply – not strive after vast material possessions and complicated apparatus. There will be enough food for everybody – for everybody prepared to work honestly for it, that is. We will contrive to make enough warm clothes, to build enough houses – cut enough fuel. As you see – we'll have time and energy left over for the things of the spirit and the mind as well."

"Enough food supposes enough land. What happens when all the land is occupied again – and people look for land and can't find it?" said Hughes.

"Well," I said. "That won't be in our lifetime, John, certainly not in England. Nor our children's. There is enough good empty land in England now for every single family to have a very big holding."

"I'd agree with you," said Tony Larkin, "but we must also have industry. It must be industry that serves the peasant – not exploits him. The cultivator must be the master, finally. And industry must not be allowed to master man. Industry is for man – not the other way around. Industry must make good things – fine and beautiful things – that people really must have. Not just turn out floods of mass-produced rubbish for mass men."

"It'll be a long time," I said, "before we'll have to make many things. There'll be enough tools, cloth, stuff like that in the stricken cities and towns."

"Ah," said Jessie. "I meant to talk to you about that too, Bear. We must not just let ourselves become dependent on looted industrial things. We must – even now – start developing our own crafts and industries – like John here's been doing – in spite of his talk. When the old industrial stuff finally wears out, or rusts away, we must not be caught with no tools in our hands. And we will lose our self-respect if we wear nothing but old borrowed garments. We must learn to card wool, and spin, and weave, make leather – all the rest of it. And thank God we'll be living surrounded by natural materials again – and not that everlasting plastic."

Jean and one of our little orphan girls, whose joint turn it was that night to cook the supper, came and announced that food was ready and so the argument came to an end.

But it set me thinking, and taking action. Much against her will Jessie allowed herself to be appointed Minister of Culture. During the two years in which she held this pompous-sounding title she started many things. To take the place of the piped entertainment of the old days she started choral societies, small orchestras, weaving clubs, art clubs, dramatic clubs, poetry societies, and heaven knows what. The organisations flourished exceedingly well: for the simple reason that, when people had done the essential work of the fields and the household, there was nothing else to do. There was no television to look at – no radio. Books came into their own again. There were plenty of books. Mick Miller brought several tons of books from the ruins of London, and in any case there were books in the district. They were read again.

Prompted by me, that thirsty man, Jessie encouraged and helped the public houses, which we re-named inns. The inns took on new life. The inn-keepers brewed their own beers, they kept good fires in the winter, they had lights on even when other people were short of lighting, and the old entertainments of Merry England sprung up again. Now that the flow of piped rubbish was cut off, our old songs came back: glorious old songs of the countryside which had survived, in hiding as it were, since before the industrial revolution. People began to make new ones; there were none from America. Step-dancing revived, and melodeon playing. Hughes encouraged a violin-making industry in Gretford, and soon every inn had its fiddler. In the summer, dancing on the village green did indeed revive – maypole dancing, even Morris dancing. And why not? I had always laughed at such things: scoffed slightly at people who went in for them as phoneys. But they only seemed phoney because they were doing it in defiance, as it were, of the spirit of the age. Morris dancing I found, when I actually saw it, was damned good fun. And everybody else found it fun too: even the industrial John Hughes. It ceased to be absurd. In fact John and

I joined the Gretford Men. As the year wore on we found that we could spare children from the fields, and they began to go to school again. Sam Packard, our Minister of Education, helped and advised by various people who were interested, devised a completely new system of teaching children. They were not so much taught, as helped to read and write and do arithmetic, but their education was based on handicrafts, arts, agriculture. The aim was that every child should leave school with at least a working knowledge of all the crafts that were worth practising, and of agriculture and stockmanship, but also with a first-class knowledge of one chosen craft. Our aim – the ideal for which we were to strive – was the educated peasant-craftsman. The person who could produce his family's food from his own holding – and at the same time, turn his hand to one skilled craft, to produce superbly some article that his neighbours wanted, and was, withal, a cultured person.

One good development that happened that winter was a changed attitude to and use of our village churches. Excepting for the dreary little wooden village halls that some villages had, there was no public building of any size and, with all the new activities that were starting up of a communal nature (people seemed to want to do things together more; it might have been some sense of insecurity, and loneliness, that we felt, due to the disruption of society) large public buildings were necessary.

The first trouble blew up with the Gretford Choir. They went to the vicar and asked him if they could use Gretford Church for a concert. He said yes – but imposed so many conditions that they were incensed. They were not, for example, to rehearse in the church, nor to sing any secular music. Young Sam Packard, who was an agnostic and a keen member of the choir, brought up the suggestion at our council meeting that the church should be thrown open to all the people.

"Look," he said. "Our church was built seven hundred years ago by Gretford people. All the people – not just one clique. Now it is reserved for the sole use of a tiny handful. How many people really go to church? Ten per cent? Not even that I should think. Why should it be for the sole use of one sect? There are Catholics in the village – they can very well claim that it is their church. It was built by their church – not by Protestants. In the Middle Ages the church belonged to the people. It was their public building. A village needs a big public building – how can we have any corporate life without one? And here in England nearly every single village has one fine public building – and it belongs to the whole village – not to just ten per cent of it . . ."

"It belongs to God," said the vicar.

"All right – it belongs to God. But do you think he would deny its use to ninety per cent of the people?"

"It's built for his worship. All are welcome."

"Then let us all worship Him in it – in our own fashions. My worship is to try and make good music. Look – there isn't going to be any flocking back to the Church of England, whatever you think. The Baptists have made some strides since the CRASH – not the C of E. Let us seize our churches, each in the name of the villagers of the parish, in the name of God. The village council will maintain the building, will decide what shall and what shall not be done in it. The Church of England parsons will have as much right as anybody else to use it, and conduct services there, but so will the nonconformists and the Catholics. And we'll be able to use our churches in the way they were meant to be used: as meeting places, theatres, concert halls, all the rest of it."

"West of the screen," I hastily put in.

"I think the idea is monstrous!" said Sir Charles.

In the end we had a referendum on it.

That was the thing about a democracy as small as ours. It was fairly easy to allow every interested person to vote on any important subject. The vote was overwhelmingly in favour of throwing open the churches. And after that we watched our churches – some of the most glorious buildings ever to be built anywhere – change from dead monuments to live institutions. They seemed to come alive, after the sleep of centuries. The vicar was absolutely furious, but he was forced, in the end, to practise the virtue of resignation. And with the church as a magnificent centre and focus, each village seemed to take on new life.

At Michaelmas, after the end of the war with the army, we had the great conference at Willingham Castle to set up the East Anglian Federation.

It was decided that districts such as ours would be set up wherever there was enough people: groups of six or seven villages, more or less – and that they should be called "hundreds". Ours became the Gretford Hundred. Democracy should be based on the Village Council, at which every man and woman could vote: the Hundred Council chosen by the Villages. The Hundred Council would be autonomous in most things: a kind of city-state – with "city" meaning a big village surrounded by smaller ones. Each Hundred would send a representative to the Great Council of East Anglia, however, and this council would decide matters relating to currency, higher education (there was to be a university), defence, foreign trade, main transport systems.

After colossal argument it was decided to establish the capital of East Anglia at Beccles.

Norwich was too vast an expanse of empty, broken and abandoned buildings to be considered. Beccles was not too damaged, was fairly central, but above all was on the water. For we realised that a lot of our trade in future, as it was in the remoter past, was going to be water-borne. Sea-going sailing barges could be got to Beccles, and a wide area of country could be reached readily by sailing river wherries, which would no doubt soon be built. A university would be built up at Beccles.

It was hoped to re-start the ancient printing industry at Bungay and resume the publishing of books, and this is the reason this book is being written.

We intended our literature to continue: not just stop where it had been when the CRASH came.

We discussed many things at that meeting.

The representatives of the other communities all agreed to model themselves largely on Gretford Hundred. We had had a head start on them; and our system seemed to be working. Trade was discussed. Some Hundreds had things that others wanted. We had timber, for example, and salt herring. Aldeburgh had re-started its brickworks. We could exchange timber for bricks. Loddon Hundred, in Norfolk, had the raiding of the ruins of Norwich. We could send barge-loads of pines up to Lodden in exchange for useful things from Norwich. The King's Lynn men had – driven by the hatred of darkness – started a sealing industry in the Wash. They would trade seal-oil, which burnt very well in lamps, for things they wanted. There were tens of thousands of seals in the Wash, but they would be cropped, not exterminated.

Canals and navigable rivers were to be re-opened. The Gipping was to be re-opened again in Stowmarket; the Stour to Sudbury; the Little Ouse to Thetford. There was even talk of one day joining the Little Ouse to the Waveney.

Defence did not seem to be an important issue, for there was no imminent threat now that the Midland army had been defeated. But it was agreed that each Hundred would have an armed citizenry and that there might eventually be a very small mobile regular strike force controlled from Beccles. But there was a lot of opposition to that. We were all agreed to keep government, on every level, to the minimum. We did not want a lot of government machinery and government interference. We were to be societies of peasants, and peasants are honest and self-sufficient, and do not want a lot of laws.

After the conference we sent messages to the people in Essex, telling them of what we had done, and also to the people the other side of the Wash, who had their headquarters in Lincoln. We eventually received replies which indicated that much the same sort of thing was happening in those areas.

There were those who were afraid that it would end up with internecine wars between the various areas of England. I have no fear of this. We are not ignorant tribesmen. We are survivors of one of the most highly civilised nations on Earth. We have no urge to go to war – no desire to attack each other. Gone is the dream of a military government of the whole country. Government is to be by consent, in small and manageable areas, and people are able to talk matters of mutual interest over amicably.

And now, as I write this – this is how things have worked out. It seems hard to believe that there was ever a war between Englishmen and Englishmen. I don't think there will ever be another.

Epilogue

by Bob Hurlock

Well yesterday was my birthday, June the Fifteenth *20 - -*.Susan (13) brought my tea up to me in the morning. Diana (20) didn't accompany her – because she's married. She married Dickie Quantrill. Dickie has his own smallholding now, down by the estuary. Like most of us – he's something else besides a farmer. He always loved the sea and he's a fisherman. Not a full-time one – he only goes fishing when there are a lot of fish about, such as at herring time, or spratting, or sea-trout in the summer. He has a fish weir in the Mudde (he and I jointly own it) which supplies us with flat fish the whole year round. Diana spends some of her time making nets for him – she makes enough to sell some to other people.

Jean (17) is courting strong: a boy from Yeldham Ferry. His family came from the Midlands and settled there on a holding we gave them. They have started a paper factory. At present they make use of the reeds from the Mudde, but they are experimenting with hemp. They hope to make that their main raw material. Robin and Susan still go to school. Of our five orphans: two, Micky and Jill, married each other and we set them up on a smallholding and with a windmill. If I lift my head I can see the mill sails turning away, through my window. She is a primitive mill: like one of the mills there used to be in the Mediterranean, with canvas sails on rough poles. But she works. The other three orphans, two boys and a girl, have left school and help us at home. Billy, one of the boys, is a weaver, and has a loom in his bedroom. The other boy wants to do nothing else but farm – and make up what I can only describe as – primitive – poetry. Marlene, the girl, has her work cut out in the house and dairy. Jessie, is nearly a full-time seed-grower now. We send her seeds all over East Anglia, and even beyond. We both gave up politics last year. Gretford Hundred had an election, but we both declined to stand. Neither of us wanted to grow into elder statesmen.

People often ask nowadays: are we better or worse off than before? I have no doubt as to what the answer is. Of course everybody has to work a lot harder. But we are all working for ourselves. And our work is varied. No-one has to do the same old dull job all day. There is constant variety in our work. We are well fed now – better, I think, than before. True we don't get things like oranges and bananas, but we have our own good fruit, and it is fresh. We don't get salads in the winter-time, but we manage to have good green vegetables. There is plenty of meat now. Everybody kills and cures his own bacon. Everybody kills an occasional sheep, and divides the meat among his neighbours. Everyone keeps poultry; and from my bedroom window I can see white geese grazing on the marshes with the sheep and cattle. Nearly everyone has at least one cow. But the greatest advantage of our present time, I think, is the absence of financial worry. People just do not seem to be interested in money any more. There is no "hire-purchase". There are no washing machines – let's face it people just have to get over the copper and the dolley-tub and do their washing themselves. It does not seem to do them any harm. It does them less harm than worrying about hire purchase payments used to do. We have no overdrafts from the bank. We have no stocks and shares and limited companies. Some of us lent material and money to old Mick Miller to start his shipyard with, and the Council helped him by guaranteeing him food for five years while he started, but that is all. People are not ambitious for material things any more. It would be no use. They want to have a good living, for themselves and their families, and be able to follow their hobbies and pursuits – all pursuits which do not require expensive and elaborate equipment.

Leisure? Surprisingly there seems to be enough of it, though not as much as before. But anyone who travelled in peasant countries before the CRASH may have found himself surprised at the amount of leisure the peasants had. It does not take long to grow sufficient food to feed a family. It is only when you have to grow enough food to feed a hundred other families too – families who live in huge cities making all sorts of gadgets that you think you need – or people just living on the dole – that you have to work hard growing food. We go along quite pleasantly. An acre of land grows more than enough wheat to keep a family throughout the year – and with a pair of good horses it takes a day to plough an acre on this light land We "don't take a lot of harm" as they say about here.

Post-Epilogue

by Dike Randle

(Recorded by Eliza Keeble)

Well naathin' 'on't do they say but I've got to have the last word – and I hoop thass goin' to be the last word too because I've got something more to do than to sit here a'dictating a lot o' squit to you much as I like you Eliza and if your father hadn't got there first I might a' bin your Dad.

Well you ask me what thass like now.

The best thing I reckon I can do is describe just what we can both of us see together out of this study window of oud Bob's.

Well thass upstairs and that look right down across the higher ground – and down to the marshes, and then the sea wall, and then we can just see the shingle bank beyond it, and then the sea. That must be one o' the master views in Suffolk – I reckon oud Bob chose this farm because he liked that view.

Before the CRASH you'd ha' looked out of that window and seen nothing but the view as you might say. Over there on the right you'd ha' sin Gretford Yacht Club, with the masts of a lot of oud Tupperware b'uts an' a few bigger yachts a'lyin' at moorings. Now there's the oud *Suffolkman* a'lyin' at anchor, and a huge new shed, built of rusty oud corrugated iron, which is Mick Miller's new shipyard. There's a big schooner a'buildin' in there and a smaller one just completed lyin' on the grid outside. Thass goin' to be larnched next Monday and Susan Hurlock's a'goin' to larnch her. That'll be a piss-up do we never see another.

Out to sea I can see several big yachts a'sailin' up and down outside the Dudgeon Bank. There was no shortage o' them after the CRASH and God knows where the owners were. They were there for the taking. Mick Miller tell me they aren't a'mucher for cargo but they use 'em for fishing. Some of 'em goo to the Farne Islands after seal oil.

Come ashore and thass whully altered. All that land beyond the ru'd was London Farming land. That was a great empty prairie – there warn't a hedge or a tree on it. Now thass cut up into ten acre plots with new-planted, quick-thorn hedges. Before you might ha' sin one tractor a'sarnterin' up an' down with one lonely man in it listenin' to the stereo. Now I can see half a hundred people! I can see two teams of heavy horses haulin' hay and – what – five or six teams of oxen. There's people cuttin' hay with the scythe, there's a wonderful conjuration of John Hughes thass an ox-drawn hay mower. That fare to be a'workin' too. There's folks a'ploughin' and a'settin' o' rape and tarnips and other late crops. The land's a patch-work o' different colours and crops whereby in the ould days it's just be barley, naathin' else. There's small belts o' baby trees planted and spinneys – folks want to have their own firewood and they want 'em for wind breaks.

Not all the folks out there are a'workin' on their own holdings. A lot on 'em are people from outside the area what are a'workin' their way to citizenship as Bob calls it. They got to do three years workin' for somebody else and work well – afore they git their own piece o' land. Then they're citizens of Gretford Hundred and if they want one they can keep a rifle under the bed and are enrolled in the Home Guard. Afore that they're on trial as you might say.

Whereas afore you wouldn't see a house from this window – now I can count a couple o' dozen! One of 'em's my own house. I built it of beach pebbles from the shingle beach and thass a job I don't want again in a hurry. No cement either – just burnt lime and mud. Cement's a thing o' the past. But I can see smoke a'comin out of a dozen chimneys as the ol' women are a'cookin' the lunch. Houses are going up all over the place. Anyone who gets a piece of land can build a house on it – no arguments. Thass a peopled countryside now. And I can see four windmills a'turnin' around – three pumpin' water and one a'grindin' wheat.

The marshes, that all belonged to London Farming, are common grazing now. Anyone in Gretford Parish has a right to put stock on 'em. I can see from here – cattle and sheep and hosses and geese. But if we have a right so we have a duty and we all have to spend a week out there on the sea-wall come winter, with a wheelbarrow and a shovel a'mendin' the bank.

Wass that – grub? Well we don't get no lemons nor oranges nor avocado pears. But we got plenty o' good apples and pears and plums and raspberries and such like. Nearly everybody grow some. There's plenty o' vegetables, much better than there used to be – and plenty o' meat. Everyone cures bacon and there's plenty of good lamb and beef. Plenty o' beer – and thass master good beer too – much better'n that piss-an'-wind we used to git. (Excuse my language but you're used to it now, Eliza dear.) We fare all right. None of us take right a lot o' harm!

Money? Well we have our Gretford money but thass bein' superseded by the East Anglian pound. Pounds, shillings and pence again like we allus did have. But we don't fare to worry about it much. Thass still used – it's still nice to hev a shillin' in your pocket – "a shillin', a shut-knife and a piece o' string" we allus used to say a man should never be without. But there's less worry about money these days. When you gets your piece o' land you gets a lot o' help – animals to stock it with – seed – help with a house. After that it's up to you. There's no hire-purchasism. Thass a thing o' the past. We aren't a posh nation! There's several good boot-makers set up and tailors and that but I 'on't say we was posh anymore. That don't worry nobody – leastwise that don't worry me.

Work? Well there's a hell of a lot of it. That never seem to finish. But nobody seem to mind – we're all a'working for ourselves you see! Better'n working for London Farming. An' thass interesting work – thass fun, do we 'ouldn't do it. Leastways I like it. I don't think some o' them toffs and retired people take to it very kindly though, but they got to put up with it. And there's plenty o' leisure too. We do have time to rejoice.

And there's more – what shall I say – fellowship. We're all in the same b'ut together and we helps each other and makes some fun.

An' I tell you what – we hear a sound now we never heard in the tractor days. And thass people a'whistlin' and a'singin' about their work. I bet you half o' them people out there on those fields are a'whistlin' and a'singin'. And another thing we hear that'd practically become a thing o' the past. And that's the birds.

Yes, like that song they sing down at the oud *Barge Inn*: *"The Larks they sing melodious at the dawning of the day!"*

About the Retriever

John Seymour went to Africa at the age of twenty and lived in the bush for thirteen years. During the years of the Second World War, he served in the East African forces as an infantry officer, first in Ethiopia and then in Burma.

After the War he found it hard to settle down; he returned to India and, then, to Africa. He moved to Suffolk, then to West Wales, running smallholdings or a small farm, and producing most of his own food. He now lives in Ireland, and runs courses on self-sufficiency on a small piece of land on the bank of a large river.

He has written many books on a great variety of subjects.